foundations - a survival guide for junior doctors

foundations

a survival guide for junior doctors

editor: Laurence Crutchlow

Foundations
– a survival guide for junior doctors

Editor Laurence Crutchlow
© 2011 CMF
All rights reserved.

Published by Christian Medical Fellowship
6 Marshalsea Road, London SE1 1HL, UK
www.cmf.org.uk

ISBN 978-0-906747-43-8

Printed by Yeomans
Design by S2 Design & Advertising - enquiries@s2design.co.uk

contents live

contents
think

act

work

notes
to overseas readers

The articles which have provided the words for this book have all been published by CMF UK, mostly during the first decade of the 21st century. The following notes aim to help readers overseas understand a little of the UK context at the time of writing.

GOD'S WORD DOESN'T CHANGE

God's word is the same wherever we are in the world. Ethical principles derived from the Bible are the same, whether in London, Cape Town, Beijing or Santiago. But of course the context does differ. Healthcare systems vary widely – there are even variations between different regions in the UK. The law varies from country to country, as do the health needs of the population, and models of medical training. 'Christian culture' also varies from country to country. Whilst our underlying view of the cross or resurrection should not differ, the way in which we express it might. There are some issues of variance within and between countries – for example whether it is acceptable for Christians to drink alcohol, or whether Christians should support capital punishment. Models of church leadership often vary.

THE UK CONTEXT

The UK is often described as a 'post-Christian' society – one where large numbers of people claimed to be Christians in the past, but where the church's influence is decreasing. This may be in stark contrast to your home, where Christians may be a persecuted minority, or conversely churches may be thriving and multiplying.

Healthcare in the UK is provided mostly through the 'National Health Service' (NHS). The NHS is government funded through general taxation, and the services are largely provided by government run organisations (although there is increasing non-government involvement). Most junior doctors will work exclusively within the NHS, with little scope for practising outside it ('privately') until they finish their specialist training. Many felt that the NHS was founded on largely Christian principles, but it has become a more challenging organisation for a Christian to work in over the years.

UK MEDICAL TRAINING

Where this book refers to a 'foundation year' or FY1 / FY2 doctor, this is a doctor who has just qualified, following usually 5-6 years of medical training - the equivalent of an 'intern' in many countries. Following these two 'foundation years', doctors may apply to train as a general (family) practitioner (GP), or as a hospital specialist. Training schemes last anywhere between three and eight years, depending on specialism chosen. At the end of this period, doctors become either a consultant in their chosen specialty, or a GP. There are other models, and some doctors work as 'staff grades' or 'associate specialists' without necessarily completing full postgraduate training.

USING THE BOOK OVERSEAS

Since most of the writing is in a UK context, some things may seem different, or need further thought to apply to your situation. However, discussions amongst junior doctors at ICMDA conferences suggest that although the exact issues facing junior doctors vary from place to place, the underlying principles needed to deal with them are much the same. It is in this knowledge that I hope this book will prove a blessing and a stimulus to further thought and prayer, wherever it is read.

Dr Laurence Crutchlow, *Editor*

preface

'So then, just as you received Christ Jesus as Lord, continue to live in him, rooted and built up in him, strengthened in the faith as you were taught, and overflowing with thankfulness... Whatever you do, work at it with all your heart, as working for the Lord, not for men... since it is the Lord Christ you are serving'.

Colossians 2:6, 3:23, 24.

The pressures on Christian junior doctors are immense. There are the social pressures of being away from the support of home, family, friends and church.

There are psychological pressures arising from the effort to maintain self esteem while struggling to acquire new skills in a high demand environment. Long hours, lost sleep and superficial contacts with large numbers of staff and patients can fuel a lethal mix of tiredness and loneliness.

Then there are the spiritual pressures of finding and adjusting to a new church and a new circle of friends, the difficulty of maintaining a devotional life and the enticing opportunity to create a new identity for oneself and compromise morally.

This is a book conceived by juniors, written for juniors by juniors past and present and addressing juniors' issues.

Throughout you will find over 70 articles by 40 authors, peppered with punchy testimonies, prayer points and 'think it through' questions which provide an opportunity for further thought, either individually or as a group.

The four-fold theme '**Live**, **Think**, **Act** and **Work**' provides the framework for the contents. There are pieces on homeopathy and heartsink patients, surviving night shifts and sharing faith, bullying and brain death, pornography and prayer, all wrapped up in biblical reflection.

Much of the material has appeared beforehand in CMF publications like *Nucleus* and *Triple Helix* but it has been reworked, re-edited and freshly presented in bite-sized portions for easy digestion.

The attractive design is quite different from anything we have ever produced. It's meant to be picked up and dipped into again and again, and left out on the coffee table to be read, shared and re-read.

Our aim was to provide a Christian medical equivalent of the *Oxford Handbook of Clinical Medicine*, with concise, accurate and easy-to-find information on a wide variety of subjects.

This book has had a long gestation; eight years from start to finish under three editors – Caroline Bunting, Rachael Pickering and Laurence Crutchlow. It's been a long time coming and a real labour of love. But I'm sure you will agree it's been well worth waiting for.

Savour, study and browse. But most of all enjoy!

Dr Peter Saunders *is Chief Executive of CMF*

acknowledgements

This book was first thought of by CMF's Junior Doctors' Committee in the early 2000s. Ideas were gathered from those attending CMF Junior Doctors' Conferences at the time, and from CMF's Publications Committee. The names of all those who contributed at this stage are too numerous to list here, but thanks are expressed.

Particular thanks are due to Caroline Bunting and Rachael Pickering, who were successively managing editors of this book before I took the project on in 2009.

In the final production process, Andrew Fergusson, Catherine Butcher and Philip Nicolls have offered editorial support, and Darren Southworth of S2 Design & Advertising has designed the book.

The CMF Junior Doctors' Committee have remained involved throughout, with Katherine Brown and Andrew Flatt providing comment and approval of the text as it was produced, and previously Eugenia Lee sourcing numerous testimonies.

Sincere thanks go to the original authors for allowing us to edit and re-publish their work, and to many junior doctors who have contributed testimonies. We have endeavoured to contact all authors to approve re-publication and editing of their work. In the few cases where we've been unable to do so, we offer our apologies, and trust that what has been produced is a true reflection of the original intention of the writing

Dr Laurence Crutchlow, *Editor*

The CMF Junior Doctors' Committee comprises junior doctor volunteers, with members' roles varying across student ministry, overseas ministry, prayer, publications, conference planning and representation to CMF executive and other organisations. It meets in CMF headquarters, London, four times a year and continues to offer exciting opportunities for involvement in fulfilling CMF objectives: pastoral support of Christian doctors, promotion of evangelism in the medical workplace, and raising awareness of biblical ethics in modern medicine. The JDC acts as both a think-tank for initiatives in the above areas, and an organiser of events – notably the annual Junior Doctors' Conference. In common with CMF itself, it is proud to involve junior doctors across specialties and with diverse skills united in love for Christ.

Dr Andrew Flatt, *CMF Junior Doctors' Committee*

introduction

Each double-page spread in this book deals with a specific topic. No two topics are quite the same... but some share common themes. Most pages are shortened versions of previously published CMF material. The original sources are identified and weblinked wherever possible, enabling interested readers to look for further information and references.

We haven't fully referenced each article in this book, but important links and suggestions for further reading are given at the end of the book, with full references available by going back to the original article online.

In a few sections, new writing has been undertaken where pre-published material was no longer relevant. In these cases there is no weblink, which is made clear on the pages concerned.

Testimonies have been written by a wide variety of Christian doctors who have faced some of the situations described.

Think-it-over sections have been put together by the editor to help readers apply the writing to their day to day work, and are intended for use either by individuals, or as a starting point for discussions in junior doctors' groups.

Bible verses are included on most pages and have been chosen to remind readers of scriptural messages relevant to the topics covered. Quotations are from the 1984 version of the NIV unless otherwise indicated.

Dr Laurence Crutchlow, *Editor*

Ambition is the last refuge of failure.
Oscar Wilde

ambition

Medicine is a well-paid profession with many opportunities for a varied career, but it can also be practised selfishly in a non-Christian manner. If you are not careful, it can become your god. On the other hand, medicine is a wonderful opportunity to serve others. It is very humbling to experience the trust and confidence patients will put in you.

The term 'ambition' is often used in a derogatory sense to suggest selfishness; doing a job only for what you can get out of it. However, ambition is not necessarily wrong. Indeed, Christians should be ambitious for their Lord in seeking to further his kingdom. The Apostle Paul had tremendous ambition and his use of sporting metaphors rings true with the ambitious athletes of today. But Paul makes it absolutely clear that his aspirations are based not in this life but in heaven. In our lives we must also make sure that God is our alpha and omega, the first and the last; our ultimate priority in all that we do.

Should Christians aim for the top in medicine?

It all depends what we mean by 'the top'! God's hierarchy is not necessarily the same as the profession's. The top for you is the place where God wants you – where you can best use your talents and gifts to serve him through the practice of medicine. Different positions give different, not necessarily better, opportunities. A clinical student is often closer to the patient than a professor and in some branches of medicine (eg pathology) the doctor is serving the patient indirectly. Some posts provide the opportunity to influence health policy whereas others have influence at a one-to-one level.

The late **Alan Johnson** wrote as Professor of Surgery in Sheffield

Ambition and service need not be opposites, but a right attitude to our careers (and lives in general) depends on a very real faith. The Bible reassures you that God will make your paths straight, providing you 'trust in the Lord with all your heart and lean not on your own understanding; (and) in all your ways acknowledge him' (Proverbs 3:5-6).

A right attitude to our careers depends on a very real faith

What sacrifices should I make to further a medical career?
What limits should I put on my medical ambitions?

All worthwhile jobs and achievements involve sacrifice and it must be calculated and counted just as Jesus recommended to those thinking of following him in the first place. But voluntary sacrifice is different from involuntary neglect of other responsibilities. Medicine can be very seductive. Limits do need to be set on both time and energy. It is easy for specific Christian service, family and recreation to be squeezed out with the excuse that 'all activity is Christian activity'. My personal limits have meant not planning academic or hospital activity on a Sunday except for emergency cover (plus not allowing the *BMJ* into the bedroom!)

There will be competition and episodes of hectic activity, but a Christian career should be hallmarked by a calm faith in God's plan and a confidence that you are in the right place to use your particular gifts in God's service.

Nucleus, July 2000. www.cmf.org.uk/publications/content.asp?context=article&id=293

'O have no spur to prick the sides of my intent, but only vaulting ambition, which o'erleaps itself, and falls on thother...'
William Shakespeare

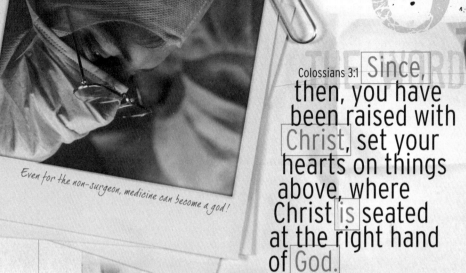

Even for the non-surgeon, medicine can become a god!

testimony

Peter says... As I grew up I was considered quite smart (including by myself, unfortunately). I developed a serious arrogance problem, and fairly strong ambition – to be professor of medicine or similar. Shortly after graduation I moved to the UK – initially as a temporary step, which has now become permanent.

Every planned career-enhancing step has somehow failed. I had to leave a hospital specialty I really liked. I did not get any of the academic posts I was craving for. I failed several exams on multiple occasions. I have become a lowly GP (quite contrary to my plans), initially in a rough part of Glasgow and now in a remote part of the Scottish Highlands.

Do I consider myself a failure? Far from it. God has been incredibly patient and generous. I have learned to become a lot more humble and to concentrate on what God wants from my life. God prepared me throughout my life for the tasks he set me and made clear that I should focus on these, rather than on my own ideas of achievement and personal glory.

Colossians 3:1 **Since, then, you have been raised with Christ, set your hearts on things above, where Christ is seated at the right hand of God.**

TAKE HOME MESSAGE: **The 'top' for you is the place where God wants you**

think it over...

1 What are my current career plans?

2 When did I last spend time reflecting on these in the light of where God wants me to be?

3 What sacrifices do I currently make in order to pursue a medical career?

4 Where should I draw my limits on the time and energy I will devote to medicine?

Finding Christian fellowship

Frequent moves as a junior doctor may mean several changes of church. I want to suggest two practical questions you need to ask of any church you're considering attending:

- Does it teach people the Bible?
- Can I bring my mates?

These questions need some unpacking. But before we do that, let's remind ourselves that the goal is to glorify God, that God is glorified as his kingdom grows, and that God does the work of growing his church. Growth is both in breadth as more people turn to Christ, and in depth as each believer becomes more like Christ.

Why is Bible teaching important, and what does it mean?

God's Word is the means by which he grows his kingdom. Throughout the whole Bible, it's God's Word that creates, sustains, sanctifies. It grows God's people. It's why the church of Acts 2 was devoted to the teaching of the apostles, and why the apostles in Acts 6 devoted themselves to the ministry of the Word. Paul stresses again and again to Timothy the importance of Word-ministry. For us today, this means that faithful Bible teaching is essential. When we choose a church, we should look for one that is teaching the Bible in all its activities and through all its members.

This leads us to the second point. Because of course, we shouldn't just 'teach the Bible'. We should teach people the Bible. The emphasis mustn't just be on the transmission but on the reception, not just on being faithful to the Bible, but on being helpful to the hearer. When we choose a church, we need to consider how it communicates the message of God's Word to the people who meet there.

Giles Cattermole wrote as CMF Head of Student Ministries

Some churches will be better at reaching students, some better with families, some with internationals, and so on. The building they meet in, the types and timings of meetings, the sort of music, the clothes the pastor wears, all these and more, are not matters of 'right and wrong', but they may be matters of wisdom. It's vital to remember that church is not just about you: it's about other people. And that means non-Christians as well as Christians.

faithful Bible teaching is essential

Whatever our mission field is, we need to consider the people we want our church to reach with the Gospel. If your friends are from very traditional backgrounds, an informal free church might be inappropriate. If your friends speak English as a second language, perhaps a church that uses old versions of the Bible might be unhelpful. If they love music, perhaps a church that has good music would be preferable over one that doesn't.

Looking back at our two questions, the first is absolute. If a church does not teach people the Bible, don't go there. The second is relative; it will depend on how well a particular church reaches you and your friends. Go somewhere that will most effectively help you bring your friends to Christ. Pray for discernment and wisdom!

testimony

Ranti says... we are not on the planet for ourselves. We are here for God's glory. We can do our thing by ourselves but we are much more effective and protected if we do it with others. We are in a battle, and who wants to be alone on a battlefield? Sometimes Christian fellowship is not so easy to find and maintain. It requires us to be vulnerable so we can be real. It requires a listening and teachable heart to hear both God and others. It requires love which covers over the hurts that we all give each other. It requires us to reach out to others who are on a limb and draw them in.

Charles says... Having a good, supportive church is the difference between make or break as a junior doctor. I never believed this could be the case, but then I didn't know how big the transition between university and working life would be. I made church an absolute priority as a junior because I knew if I wasn't worshipping God weekly with other Christians I would suffer spiritually.

I tried going to church after each night shift, praying that I would have some rest, and if not ask God for concentration – I only fell asleep during one sermon. I led a house group as a junior doctor and while shift work meant you had to be good at delegating I found the friends in that group to be such a support to me.

Friends forever

Hebrews 10:25 Let us not give up meeting together, as some are in the habit of doing, but let us encourage one another – and all the more as you see the Day approaching.

TAKE HOME MESSAGE: **Fellowship with other believers is vital to surviving and thriving as a junior doctor**

think it over...

1 In the last month, in how many weeks have you been able to attend at least one church activity (ie Sunday service, mid-week house group etc)?

2 Is the teaching of scripture central to your church's meetings?

3 Is your church somewhere that you could take an interested non-Christian colleague?

cmf can help...

An annual junior doctors' conference along with 'open house' meetings in towns and cities across the countries help busy young doctors to maintain fellowship with other believers facing similar struggles. See www.cmf.org.uk/fellowship/juniors for local contacts. If there isn't a group in your area, why not start one?

The CMF office will also put Foundation Year doctors in touch with older local doctors who can provide care and support... please contact CMF for further details.

dating

I 've sometimes wondered how many years you can live through thinking that sooner or later you will meet your life partner.

As a youngster you assume 'it' will happen, either at university or somewhere along the way. Then, as you get older, you realise you could easily go another ten years waiting for 'it' to arrive. As a Christian woman, it's tempting to think that being single is caused by the lack of single men in the church and the limited circles from which to choose, compared to our non-Christian girlfriends. But it is a bit more complex than that.

Statistics do indicate that things are hardest for Christian women. At least a quarter of adult church attendees are single women, whilst single men make up only a tenth. However, it's not just Christian women finding it difficult to meet a partner. The 2001 census showed that 30 percent of all adults remain single, with up to 51 percent of Londoners going it alone. Western society as a whole is experiencing a change in the way our relational futures develop.

Is it time to get proactive? The number of Christian online dating facilitators is growing fast. Christian speed dating and singles' dinners are also increasingly popular. They expand the pools of Christians with whom to develop friendships and possibly relationships. Many of us feel that they are perfectly okay for Christians but others have strong reservations:

Jacky Engel wrote as CMF Research and Publications Assistant

How am I judging the guy sat opposite me for three minutes? Paul said that young men must treat young women like their sisters, and I'm sure the opposite applies! Proactively pursuing a relationship in this way may breed discontent. 'God is most glorified in us when we are most satisfied in him.'

The biggest danger is idolising the notion of being in a relationship.

(Anonymous junior)

Most of us continue to survive because we're convinced that... with grit and determination... we will end up in some magical union. It's a form of religion

Simply getting married does not guarantee a happy-ever-after. It's a mistake to think, for instance, that our sexual struggles will be over once we're married. Anna shares her story:

Sexual purity as a Christian junior is tough. You spend a lot of time away from Christian contacts and are forced into close relationships with colleagues. Tiredness and shift work loneliness can be overwhelming and admiration for a colleague's clinical skills can turn into romantic attachment. I have watched two of my Christian juniors drift away from God via such affairs.

Even a romantic relationship with a fellow believer is no guarantee of a happy-ever-after. A smug married myself, I managed to fall for a non-Christian colleague. After a really painful time, the remnants of my underlying faith brought me back to right relationships with my husband and God. Looking back, it probably wouldn't have happened had I spent more time on God's word, prayer and my marriage. Instead, I'd let doctoring come first. Whatever your marital status, keep your relationship with God as your number one priority.

LINKS *Triple Helix, Autumn 2006. www.cmf.org.uk/publications/content.asp?context=article&id=1863*

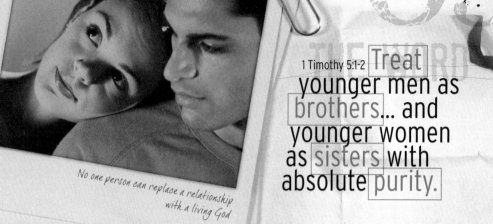

Let me not to the marriage of true minds admit impediments.
William Shakespeare

No one person can replace a relationship with a living God

testimony

Claire got proactive... First of all I tried speed-dating – but only once! It proved a dismal experience with everyone trying to make an impression and saying ridiculous things. I really couldn't find out about anyone's personality or interests. Writing a personal advert proved more inspiring. It was a good way to date men from different professions. Of course you only meet one person at a time with adverts, and I stumbled across the perfect compromise solution when I heard about singles' dinners. It was much more natural than speed dating and at the very first dinner I met my husband-to-be. The rest, as they say, is history!

1 Timothy 5:1-2 Treat younger men as brothers... and younger women as sisters with absolute purity.

TAKE HOME MESSAGE: **There is more to dating than tactics...**

cmf can help...
Marriage isn't the only way!
See Live 10 for a consideration of singleness

think it over...

1 What are my motives for dating and wanting to be married?

2 What, if anything, puts me off the thought of 21st century dating techniques?

3 What are my preconceptions about married life? Consider these Bible verses and apply their principles to dating:
a) Proverbs 31:30 – look for character
b) Romans 12:10-11 – develop friendships
c) Hebrews 10:24 – maintain accountability
d) Philippians 4:12 – be content
e) Philippians 4:13 – seek God's help

The individual suffers from depressed mood, loss of interest and enjoyment, and reduced energy leading to increased fatiguability and diminished activity. Marked tiredness after only slight effort is common.

depression

My 'downer' is still very fresh in my mind. It lasted about four months and I felt wretched. It was the cumulative effect of being let down and 'slapped in the face' several times in unexpected ways. Each episode on its own appeared insignificant but so many things hitting me in one go were sufficient to knock me over.

Like many professionals, I covered it up to those around me, for fear of losing face. I kept telling myself I wasn't supposed to feel this way. Every morning I put on my mask of 'all is well in the world'. To everyone else I seemed my usual jolly self, but inside I felt thoroughly miserable and as soon as I got home again the mask came off. At church I wanted to scream, 'Are you all as happy as you make out to be, or does anyone feel as bad as I do?'

What brought me out of it? Firstly, I tried to assess my feelings and reactions to situations – not easy when you feel yourself spiralling down and find it difficult to remember what made you start feeling low in the first place! Secondly, I never stopped reading my Bible or going to church, even though my heart wasn't in it. I made a promise to my Dad when I was nine that I would read my Bible every day. It's important to keep reading God's word and meeting with his people because these are very often the means of keeping yourself sane and allowing God to speak to you. Don't spite yourself by cutting off some of your routes to recovery. I didn't suddenly wake up one morning and feel on top of the world. It took time. You need to allow God and time to restore you.

Roselle Ward is a GP and wrote as a CMF Student Staffworker in Northern Ireland

Christian depressives

The psalmist who wrote Psalms 42 and 43 knew what real anguish was; however, he also knew where his help lay. In 1 Kings 19, Elijah hit rock bottom and asked God if he might die; God dealt graciously with him and met his needs.

These are the actions of a loving and understanding God.

Many prominent Christians in history have been dogged with feelings of depression or anxiety: Martin Luther (reformer), John Bunyan (author), William Cowper (hymn writer), Lord Shaftesbury (human rights reformer), Christina Rossetti (poet and hymn writer), Amy Carmichael (missionary), JB Phillips (theologian) and even CS Lewis. I urge you to read their stories in *Genius, Grief and Grace* (Christian Focus Publications Ltd).

Using the Bible with sensitivity

Whilst I mentioned the role of God's word in my recovery, I warn against being tempted to 'throw' glib verses at people, just to make them (and yourself) feel better. This can be one of the most uncaring and hurtful actions. I remember dealing with a Christian man who was really quite depressed. But what made his depression worse were his Christian friends and church. They thought that he shouldn't feel like that. So week after week they would give him 'a wee verse' to cheer him up. These ill-thought actions only made his depression worse.

The book of Job teaches us to avoid being an unhelpful 'comforter'. There is a time and place for using God's word, but it must be in a caring manner. Often a hurting person just needs to know there is someone there for them.

Dealing with your own depression

Our profession has a higher than average incidence of suicide and alcoholism than the general public. There are a lot of stressed-out doctors and you need to be prepared to face this stress because it will hit you all too quickly! Warning signs include: drinking alcohol before facing work; minimising every contact with patients/colleagues so that you do

testimony

Roxy speaks from experience... I used to have a rather biased view of depression. I knew the theory but assumed that depressed people just weren't coping with life very well! I was sure I would never suffer from it – I would fight it off with the shield of faith!

Then one day it crept up on me unawares. I had been happy and busy. Gradually, I started to get stressed about work and doubt my abilities as a doctor. Before long I realised I was depressed.

What have I learned? I've discovered what depression feels like: the heaviness, exhaustion and utterly negative thoughts. I now have much more compassion for depressed patients and friends. I've stopped being prejudiced: depression is not a sign of weakness but a genuine illness. And I have learned to look after myself better. God calls us to serve and to make sacrifices, but he cares for us and does not want us to burn ourselves out.

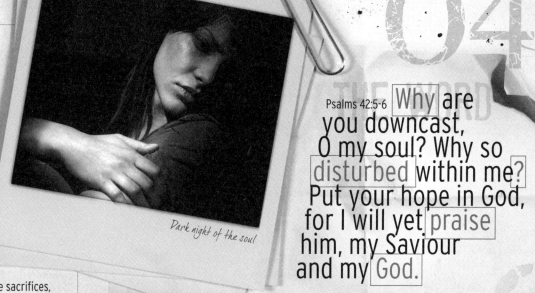

Dark night of the soul

Psalms 42:5-6

Why are you downcast, O my soul? Why so disturbed within me? Put your hope in God, for I will yet praise him, my Saviour and my God.

the bare minimum of work; inability to concentrate on the matter in hand with your thoughts entirely taken up by the workload ahead; irritability; inability to take time off without feeling guilty; feelings of excessive shame or anger when reviewing past *débacles* and emotional exhaustion.

1. Recognise that you are stressed.
   Take it seriously when a colleague points it out.
2. Confide in someone you can trust.
3. Give your mind time to rejuvenate.
4. Look at the potential causes and then try and take control:
   learn to prioritise, don't arrive late, and spread out your paperwork.
   Take time out for yourself.
5. Consult your own GP.
6. Remember the BMA has a confidential help-line.
7. Every day, read God's word and talk to him.
   He has been there before you.

think it over...

1 What support structures do you have around you?

2 What is it about being a doctor that makes diagnosing and managing depression more difficult?

3 Why do some Christians find admitting that they are depressed so difficult?

TAKE HOME MESSAGE: **Admitting you are depressed is not a sign of weakness**

> No drug, not even alcohol, causes the fundamental ills of society.
> If we're looking for the source of our troubles, we shouldn't test people for drugs,
> we should test them for stupidity, ignorance, greed and love of power.
> *P.J.O'Rourke*

drink + drugs

Misuse of alcohol and other drugs is a growing problem in Western society, and doctors and medical students are at least as susceptible to it as the rest of the population. Although doctors use 'drugs' less than they do alcohol, misuse is also a significant phenomenon. Of those with an alcohol problem, a significant proportion go on to develop a drug habit.

In the chaos of a busy clinic or ward round it is hard to have sympathy for those who are thought to have a self-inflicted illness. Even so, looking at the evidence, it is apparent that many medics know the clinical features of alcohol and drug abuse not only from textbooks and patients but from personal experience. Is the tendency not to look beyond the stereotypes protecting us from admitting our own problem?

As well as affecting our behaviour towards patients, substance misuse affects our competence in diagnosis and treatment. Signs such as withdrawal; disinterest; uncharacteristic, anti-social or impulsive behaviour; unreliability; irritability; tardiness and over-prescription are common. Although often the consequence of sleep deprivation, they may also be due to substance misuse.

People misuse alcohol and drugs for a variety of different reasons. People are neither slaves to their genetic makeup nor to environmental influences. There is always an element of choice and everyone is ultimately responsible for their own actions. Doctors are in a position of privilege, trust and responsibility and should act accordingly. However they are also human and subject to human failings.

Doctors are under the authority not only of the General Medical Council, but also of God. Perhaps the principles of our society, where anything is acceptable if you like it, are partly to blame for the state we are in. A return to the biblical idea that 'everything is permissible – but not everything is beneficial' might well help in the fight against substance abuse.

The Bible has a great deal to say about alcohol. Wine, for example, is mentioned 214 times. However, it is important to understand the context. In biblical Israel, water was not always plentiful and was often unsafe to drink. Wine was drunk with meals and for refreshment much as we now drink tea and coffee. It is not surprising then that the consumption of wine and other alcoholic drinks is not discouraged in either Testament.

There are however restrictions on the use of alcohol. Total abstinence was only encouraged for specific groups, but over-indulgence in alcohol and drunkenness are severely discouraged. The dangers of drinking in excess are often pointed out – including woe, sorrow and strife. Self-control and moderation are strongly advocated in the New Testament.

While the Bible says little explicitly about addiction, it implies a great deal. Firstly, it teaches that the only true and trustworthy answer to life's problems and stresses is found in Jesus Christ. Secondly, addictions are linked to idolatry, the worship of anything that is not God. Lastly, the behaviour caused by addiction – for example, selfishness, strife, jealousy, theft and poor stewardship of resources – is uniformly condemned throughout Scripture.

Christians believe that the ultimate answer to addiction lies in Jesus Christ. The good news of the Bible is not only that Jesus will give the strength to beat addiction; he will replace the drug as the focus of life. He will help addicts in a way drugs never could. Christians are not people who live a life without difficulties, they are people who have known God's forgiveness, and who have his help to face this life and his promise of the life to come.

Donald Inverarity
wrote as a junior doctor

LINKS *Doctors, Drink and Drugs* was published by CMF in 1997 and is available from the CMF bookstore at *www.cmf.org.uk/bookstore*. ISBN 0-906747-31-7.

testimony

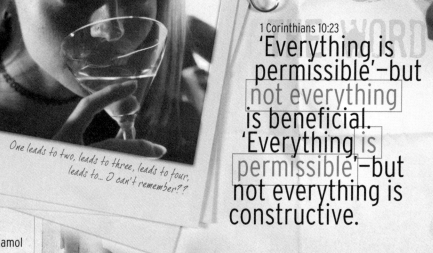

One leads to two, leads to three, leads to four, leads to... I can't remember??

An anonymous doctor writes... 'If we confess our sins, he is faithful and just and will forgive us our sins and purify us from all unrighteousness.' (1 John 1:9)

I became a Christian at medical school hoping it would help me deal with my long standing feelings of low self esteem and inferiority to others. I threw myself into good works hoping to please God but never quite fitting in with my Christian peers. A stream of addictive behaviours to work, relationships and exercise followed before finally finding prescription drugs as a hospital SHO. I struggled with nights and remaining cordial to the nurses when woken from sleep. A couple of co-codamol helped ease the stress and made me a more pleasant person to work with. This provided an immediate solution to my anxieties and I felt complete as a person for the first time in my life.

Before long, the use of codeine became a daily habit and I continued the use, losing control of the amount used as my tolerance grew. I continued using throughout my career as a GP, purchasing drugs over the counter and from the internet. With the use came the lies which got me into trouble both personally and professionally. I longed to be a faithful Christian but was not prepared to confess my drug use to the Lord and seek treatment. The decision was taken out of my hands when my senior partner found out and I had to seek help. I subsequently felt the Lord come close to me in a way I had never known possible. My self esteem was renewed as I challenged the destructive thought patterns that had led to my illness and began to discover God's plan for my life.

TAKE HOME MESSAGE: **The ultimate answer to addiction lies in Jesus Christ**

1 Corinthians 10:23

'Everything is permissible'—but not everything is beneficial. 'Everything is permissible'—but not everything is constructive.

think it over...

1 How much alcohol did you drink last week? Was it over recommended limits?

2 Would you spot an alcohol or drug problem in another doctor you worked with? If so, what would you do about it?

3 How does the knowledge that Jesus is the ultimate answer to addiction affect the way you treat patients with addictions?

finance

Neither a borrower nor a lender be,
For loan oft loses both itself and friend,
And borrowing dulls the edge of husbandry.
William Shakespeare

What is a right attitude to money? Does it matter if we follow the world's ways and allow ourselves to spend most of our careers in debt, living beyond our means?

Start thinking now about major life choices

Do you expect to live in the 1st world or the 3rd world for some or all of your working life? Do you have to be committed to a middle class lifestyle, or could you live with less? Do you expect to marry, or are you prepared to remain single (it is worth asking this question anyway as a preparation to any serious relationship!)? Do you want to have none, two, four, or even six children? Are you committed to medicine, or would you consider Christian ministry, or mission work overseas?

Who is going to decide your standard of living?

Will it be the world, with the constant inducements to unnecessary consumption? Will you hand over that major decision to the bureaucrats of the NHS, who will set the pay scales? Or will you make that decision positively for yourself? Might God the creator and sustainer of all we know have an interest in that decision?

Live within your means

In the light of the choices you make, live accordingly. If you plan to go overseas, free yourself of student debt as soon as possible, and start saving for Bible College or any other preparation you might need. Once you are earning, buy a house that is within your means (if you need to), and avoid having to pay off a mortgage for the next 25 years (unless that is part of the bigger picture). Do you need the newest, fastest, smartest set of wheels, or will something less costly serve your needs more effectively?

Giles Rawlinson
wrote as CMF Chief
Administrator

Spend on people rather than property

Practise hospitality. Are people more important than things to us? When did we last invite friends round to share even a very ordinary meal? Why not cook twice as much for the meal after your regular church service and be on the lookout for some people to invite home?

Live in the light of eternity

Three score years and ten is a very short time, while eternity goes on forever. Do we live as if it is exactly the other way round, and that this life is all there is to consider?

Christian giving should be:

- **Spiritual** – Only Christians will give for the extension of God's kingdom, and this should be our priority. Don't respond to the latest high profile celebrity appeal, but support Christian ministry with which you have a direct link.
- **Generous** – I think it was John Wesley who lived on £30 per year when his income was £100, and still lived off £30 when his income rose to £300. As a consequence, he was able to give so much more away.
- **Methodical** – Giving takes planning, so get planning! Be informed about the causes you support and don't assume they are making good use of your resources. Pray for those organisations you support; build links with specific activities, so you can really feel part of what is being done.
- **Cheerful** – Giving should be enormous fun for the giver, and the cause of real joy for the recipient. So let's make our own giving fun, rather than just a duty.

LINKS *Nucleus, 2003. www.cmf.org.uk/publications/content.asp?context=article&id=373*

testimony

Matthew says... For the Christian, the question when giving is not so much how much to give away, as how much of God's money should be kept for yourself! Starting work brings a change in income, but also an ever-growing number of outgoings. Wait and see what's left over at the end of the month to give to God's work and there might not be much, if anything, to spare.

The most helpful advice I received was prayerfully to set aside an amount early on each month. I chose to set up a regular payment into a Charities Aid Foundation account from which I could then give tax efficiently.

By budgeting sensibly with what's left over I've found that God always seems to provide enough money for what he has planned for me to do!

William says... Forward planning is essential. Incomes can fluctuate as a junior doctor with constantly changing pay bands for different rotas, or more dramatically if working as a locum.

It's very rare to be able to avoid borrowing completely. Inflated house prices mean that for most it is not realistic to buy a home without a mortgage; buying into a practice as a GP usually requires a loan. I've found it important to plan borrowing, and to know before doing it how it will be paid off. That means on the occasions I've needed to do it, I've been able to do it with confidence, knowing I'm not tied down by it.

It's well worth reviewing service costs as well. Car insurance and mobile phone costs are easy to control by reviewing your choice of provider each year; the same goes for utility bills.

It's all very well to say that you'll just give money away and sort out the consequences... but I've found I've had more money than can be used in this way when I've been careful in my financial planning first.

All that glistens is not gold

2 Corinthians 9:7 Each man should give what he has decided in his heart to give, not reluctantly or under compulsion, for God loves a cheerful giver.

think it over...

1 What action are you taking to clear debts incurred as a student?

2 Have you considered prayerfully what your future financial needs are likely to be?

3 Are you managing your finances today in the light of plans for the future?

4 How much of your income are you giving to God's work? When did you last review this?

TAKE HOME MESSAGE: **Our financial decisions speak volumes about where our priorities lie**

Happy marriages begin when we marry the one we love, and they blossom when we love the one we married.

marriage

The Bible is clear when it comes to marriage – it is created by God and is a natural state for those of his people who are called to it. Christians should see dating as a preparation for marriage, at least potentially. It can be a great blessing and stabilising factor in our otherwise busy and turbulent medical lives.

However, it is not to be taken lightly. Marriage is binding and lifelong in God's eyes. Hence, in the words of the Anglican marriage service, 'it must not be undertaken carelessly, lightly, or selfishly, but reverently, responsibly, and after serious thought.' Marriage is not necessarily what God has planned for everyone and we should remember that even such great examples as Mother Teresa, the apostle Paul and our Lord Jesus were not married. If you are considering marriage, take time alone with God to look deeply into your motives – is it because you fear being alone, feel incomplete as a person, or need to fit in within the Christian community? If any of these things could be a motive, pause and take stock.

If you do marry, it is important that the timing is correct. It should not be hastened into, but neither should it be delayed if you are both ready and it is what God has planned for you.

Even today the marriage ceremony follows an ancient pattern seen in the covenants of the Bible. It includes making promises before witnesses, giving and receiving rings as a sign of the covenant, and sharing a meal to celebrate. And as for sacrifice, an important element of ancient covenants, there's plenty of that to come!

One consideration is that junior doctors are expected to be a mobile bunch. Even registrars may be on rotations that include hospitals miles away from each other. Anyone marrying a doctor should be aware that they may have to move house frequently for the next ten years.

Chris Pollitt and **Abi Crutchlow** wrote as medical students and **Jenny Wilson** wrote as a GP

In a recent morning surgery family breakdown was a significant factor in five of six depressed patients, one of six with physical problems, one of two for medication review and two DNAs. How different the morning could have been had relationships been intact, and how many more quality points I might have been able to earn! Studies back this up. Mental health improves after marriage and deteriorates after divorce or separation. Even taking demographic factors into account children from single parent households are twice as likely to be unhappy, have low self-esteem, or mental health problems. Single mothers have poorer health than their married counterparts.

Many Christian doctors don't know about the statistics surrounding family breakdown in Britain today, let alone non-Christian colleagues. Although divorce rates have increased, once a couple have married they are far more likely to stay together than if they co-habit, especially if they marry prior to having children.

Family breakdown has huge financial implications too. In 2000 the direct cost to the UK government of family breakdown was estimated to be at least £15 billion per year (£11 per week for every taxpayer). An accountant friend worked out that a doctor who earns £70,000 a year will contribute at least £35 a week to sorting out the problems of family breakdown, the major components being for social benefits and welfare, the criminal justice system, extra costs of education, free prescriptions and lost productivity.

As Christians we have a responsibility to be aware of the problems in our society. It is not our place to judge those who are in difficulty but to approach their problems as Christ would have done. As Christian doctors we are not immune from relationship problems ourselves and perhaps even more prone as we take on others' burdens.

LINKS

Nucleus, 2006. www.cmf.org.uk/publications/content.asp?context=article&id=1798
Triple Helix, Summer 2004. www.cmf.org.uk/publications/content.asp?context=article&id=1266

testimony

Abi (a junior doctor married to another medic) **says...** Being married to another medic has its ups and downs. It is often an invaluable source of understanding and support, as non-medical Christians may not appreciate the difficulties in working odd hours and the commitments and stresses of the job. Having a spouse who understands that there will be times when home group or church is difficult to attend is refreshing and can help maintain links with church and other Christians if you are unable to attend meetings in person. As a Christian a lot of ethical dilemmas can arise in your day-to-day work as a medic, and it is good to be able to discuss these across the dinner table and seek another trusted and fresh perspective.

There are times when you can feel like ships in the night, and it is important to consider co-ordinating rotas and ensuring where possible that time is blocked out for each other, including attending church or other Christian activities - this can sometimes require great organisation!

Discussing career plans and location early on is also important if you are both medics to ensure that one partner does not 'dominate' the other, and that potential pitfalls and compromises can be identified. This can also apply to choice of church and it is worth ensuring both are comfortable attending alone as this will probably happen frequently!

Andrew (a junior doctor married to a non-medic) **says...** Ironically I presumed for a while I would marry a medic. Not that I had strong views; I just anticipated finding a partner within the adventure of medicine, sharing pursuit of knowledge and diagnostic challenges. I met my wife mid-way through medical school where we lived in the same halls and worked together in a charity group.

I find myself grateful for many reasons she isn't a medic. Just as I'm intrigued by her areas of work (writing and children's rights) she has always had an interest in science, which I'm glad to satisfy!

In marriage, each partner is God's gift to the other. Part of her gift to me has been, and is, whole worlds of literature I might never have known.

Each partner is God's gift to the other

Genesis 2:24 **For this reason a man will leave his father and mother and be united to his wife, and they will become one flesh.**

think it over...

1 If married, what steps can you take to make time for each other in a busy professional life?

2 How can we support married couples in the church?

3 How can we support marriage as doctors?

4 How might we advise a non-Christian patient who is struggling with marriage?

TAKE HOME MESSAGE: **Marriage matters to wider society, not just married couples**

You may as soon find a living man that does not breath, as a living Christian that does not pray.
— Matthew Henry

08

prayer

Doctors are not alone in leading busy lives. Jesus was busy but still took time to draw close to the Father in prayer, responsive to his word. Prayer has been described as the breath of the soul. We breathe in by the Spirit, God's *pneuma*, and breathe out our prayers in the name of the Lord Jesus. Through prayer we support each other and join in the battle against spiritual wickedness.

Just as respiration keeps us alive, so we should daily stay alive to the unseen presence of God, often saying 'thank you' as well as 'help'. Some expand on the Lord's prayer, whilst others use the '**ACTS**' sequence: approaching God with **A**we and adoration, prompting **C**onfession of unworthiness and specific sins. **T**hankfulness follows, for mercy, grace and answered prayer. **S**upplication, so often put first, comes last.

Problems in prayer

Wandering thoughts – No doubt we all know these, especially when harassed. As well as praying about the preoccupation itself, a notepad is useful for things needing attention later.

I don't feel as though I'm getting through – Assurance of God's attention is based on facts, not feelings. He has promised never to leave us and is always ready to hear our prayers. The Spirit of Jesus intervenes for us when we don't know how to pray. Praying through a psalm, finding a prayer partner or prayer meeting can all help.

I've prayed and prayed about this but God doesn't answer – Prayer must be in line with God's will. Whereas he can and does say both 'Yes' and 'No' he frequently says 'Wait'. Over time he may change our heart's desires whilst hindsight often explains his delays.

Janet Goodall wrote as an emeritus consultant paediatrician

Powerless prayer

As with literal respiration and physical dyspnoea, the vital flow of *pneuma*, the Spirit, can be impeded in comparable ways.

Airway obstruction can kill. Similarly, harboured sin blocks off the free flow of the Spirit, but repentance and confession let in the oxygen of the forgiving grace of God.

Running too fast makes us breathless. Habits of swift decision and prompt action can habituate us to approaching God hastily too. Early morning quiet is thwarted by nights on call. Lack of exercise, physical and spiritual, predisposes to dyspnoea. To drop altogether the discipline of spiritual exercise leaves us unfit for the race set before us. Nehemiah met his (often dangerous) tasks strengthened by times of earnest prayer, but his SOS prayers were effective, too.

An unbalanced diet impairs exercise tolerance by producing either obesity or malnutrition. Souls, too, become inert on junk food. 'Relaxing' for too long with TV or magazines can produce spiritual anorexia. The mind reflects what it feeds on, so if our goal is to develop the mind of Christ we must guard the input.

Carrying a heavy load can have us panting and ready to stop. When Moses felt this, he was urged to share his workload and give others a chance to grow. At times, though, on top of all else come family problems, difficult relationships, or sickness of body, mind or emotions – yet at such times, periods of concentrated prayer can be nigh impossible. We should ask others to pray for us, knowing that the Lord's own sustaining care never ends.

Prayer offered in helplessness commits the problem to the power of God. He is then able to do immeasurably more than we ask or imagine.

LINKS *Triple Helix*, Autumn 2005. www.cmf.org.uk/publications/content.asp?context=article&id=1691

Prayer does not fit us for the greater work;
prayer is the greater work.
Oswald Chambers

Prayer: the breath of the soul

Philippians 4:6 Do not be anxious about anything, but in everything, by prayer and petition, with thanksgiving, present your requests to God.

testimony

Kerry says... As a medical student I was often hideously under-prepared for my exams. As I sat in the rows of little exam tables I would always pray that God would help me through as I knew I couldn't pass on my own merits. God was faithful and I got through all my exams. As a house officer I was petrified of being alone on nights and on-calls; anything could happen to me. My lack of undergraduate study only compounded that fear. Swiftly pacing the darkened corridors between wards at night, I would pray earnestly that God would help me avoid medical disaster. Somehow, miraculously, I was kept from feeling completely out of my depth, God always saw me safely through. Not just that, but God provided some amazing Christian seniors to teach and help me at work, especially so when my home life became complicated with a seriously ill parent.

TAKE HOME MESSAGE: **Through prayer we stay alive to the unseen presence of God**

think it over...

1 What do you currently do to ensure you continue to pray when life is busy or difficult?

2 How do you plan to adapt in future - perhaps when you get married, become a GP, or have children?

3 Think through the causes of powerless prayer. Most junior doctors would identify with these to some extent. How can you combat these things?

It's important to understand the basis and nature of this addiction, not as an excuse or justification, but as a point of reference.

Pornography addictions

Christians are not immune from the pressures of living in a sex-saturated society. The UK is one of the most affected countries in the world – our porn industry is worth an estimated £1 billion share of the £20 billion world market. UK internet surfers look up the word 'porn' more than anyone in the English speaking world.

What does the Bible have to say about porn? Obviously its modern form was not known in ancient Israel, but the Ten Commandments include three very relevant edicts: 'You shall not make for yourself an idol... You shall not commit adultery... You shall not covet your neighbour's wife'. Taken together, these laws establish that God regards anything which causes a person to desire sexually anyone other than his/her spouse as totally wrong.

Heart-motivation

In the New Testament, Jesus shines the penetrating light of these commandments on our often hidden heart-motivation when he says: 'You have heard it said "Do not commit adultery". But I tell you that anyone who looks on a woman lustfully has already committed adultery with her in his heart' (Matthew 5:27-28).

It is not just our actions that matter, but also our thoughts and attitudes. Pornography threatens the integrity of sex because it encourages unfaithful thoughts and undermines marital fidelity.

Many men also testify to ongoing intrusive thoughts about other women; the remains of their pornographic past.

Chris Richards is a Consultant Paediatrician and **Trevor Stammers** wrote as a GP and lecturer in medical ethics

Freedom

How can we stay free and help our patients to do so? Remarkably, in the Christian faith there is no sin too serious, no life too awful and no person too hopeless to be beyond God's reach. Jesus has already paid the price for the worst of sins imaginable when he hung on the cross. None of us has lived the blameless life that approaches the perfect holiness of God: 'All have sinned and fallen short of the glory of God'. There are only two types of people – those who have received God's forgiveness and those who need to! There is no other way to freedom.

Nothing is hidden from God's eyes; God sees and grieves over the deeds done in dark rooms

Confession

When taking radical steps to deal with pornography, confession to God may be augmented by confession to a trusted Christian friend or counsellor. The principle of 'confess your sins to one another' can be of enormous help when dealing with sexual sin. Admitting the full extent of pornography addiction is very difficult; the temptation to hide aspects of it is always there. Fully exposing the issues means that healing can go as deep as it needs to and the chances of relapse are reduced.

'There is a way that seems right to a man, but in the end it leads to death'. (Proverbs 14:12). Pornography can seem so attractive, offering stimulation without consequences, intimacy without responsibility. But its rewards are as shallow as the page or flat screen, its reality as false as the sugary smiles and makeup, and its damage long outlasts its transient thrills.

Adapted by kind permission of Christian Vision for Men

testimony

One woman says... Based on a false image of reality, pornography brings unreal and damaging expectations into relationships; as one woman describes: 'The real reason I hated *Playboy* was that the models established a standard I could never attain without the help of implants, soft lighting and airbrushing. It's a standard that equates sexuality with youth and beauty. I didn't want him buying into this definition of sexuality. I was planning a future with this man and I wanted to feel secure in the knowledge that, even after two kids and 20 years, he would still find me sexy.'

Pornography is a parasite

1 John 1:9 **If we confess our sins, he is faithful and just and will forgive us our sins and purify us from all unrighteousness.**

A male junior doctor says... Let's face it. Two in the morning, a tired junior doctor, testosterone and a television are not a pretty combination. Be it on-call or after getting home many of us will identify with this situation, and how many times do we fall into the snare? We may not all share the same struggles as young, male Christian doctors, but one thing is for sure – we all struggle in one way or another. As John tells us, 'If we say we have no sin, we deceive ourselves...' (1 John 1:8).

Struggling with sin is often disheartening simply because it goes on and on! But as we choose to live by and be led by the Holy Spirit our lives will be different: 'Live by the Spirit, and you will not gratify the desires of the sinful nature' (Galatians 5:16). This is a wonderful promise because it encourages us to persevere and not grow weary. Inwardly as Christians, we are being renewed day by day, becoming who Jesus wants us to be.

We need to pursue and request self-control – the power to renounce ungodliness – which we, in our hearts, know leads to true freedom. Effort and rule-keeping alone will not liberate us from the sins that so easily entangle us. No, I am learning that it is a relationship with God that matters, ongoing and characterised by our persistent petitioning.

think it over...

1 What pressures (honestly) make it difficult for you to obey God's teaching about sex?

2 What steps do you / can you take to avoid being 'sucked in' to society's obsession?

3 Have you considered practical steps such as internet filters or accountability software?

4 How can you help others who find sexual images a problem?

TAKE HOME MESSAGE: **God sees all we do – freedom from addiction can only come through him**

19

Singleness

'**D**on't worry, there'll be plenty of nice boys at university', my mother said when I moaned about the lack of Christian boys in my hometown. But when I got to university, my year was 70% girls, and there was only one Christian boy. I had a couple of boyfriends through medical school, but after neither relationship worked out, I belatedly came to realise that there was more to it than finding someone I massively fancied who happened to be Christian. Jesus was positive about both marriage and celibacy – but he was adamant that a person's primary commitment should be to him rather than to a husband or wife. Paul appears to have been unmarried, and also affirms the single life in 1 Corinthians 7, whilst making it clear that there is nothing wrong with marriage.

Advantages and disadvantages

Singleness gives us time – we have longer to spend with God, and fewer family obligations. We have more freedom. The most difficult problem many of us face is *loneliness*; coming home to an empty flat, turning on the TV and eating dinner alone. Coupled with the loneliness can be a lack of accountability; few people may really see what you do with your thoughts, time or money. Another problem is getting involved with people just because they're a Christian and because they're there. Do you have similar attitudes on important issues; do you approve of the things they do with their time and money; would they make a good parent to any future children? If the answer to these things is no, then a relationship is unlikely to last and may cause considerable hurt to both of you.

How do we truly live for God in the situation he's put us in?

People tell you to trust God about your future, but what do you trust him for? God never promised that we'd get married and live happily ever after. If God is really in control, we are single right now because God has a purpose which could only be achieved this way. Even though this can be hard to come to terms with, we should accept that this is God's will for us.

There are a number of practical steps we can take to be content and fulfilled as single people in the place where God has put us:

- **God never designed us to survive on our own**, but to enjoy the church family. Church is more than a place we go to on Sunday – it is designed to be a community of believers meeting each other's needs.
- **Recognise that marriage isn't a state of eternal happiness and fulfilment**. Every human being will hurt, disappoint and let us down. Coping with life's difficulties now will prepare us for what may come, and bring recognition that it is Christ we need more than any person.
- **Be content in the situation in which God has placed you**, giving thanks for his many blessings. Although we may not have a choice over our marital status, we are in control of how we react to it – whether we spend our lives wishing for what we don't have, or get on with living.
- **Develop strong accountable friendships with other believers, married and single**. Even a spouse will never meet all our friendship needs; other relationships are important too.
- **Stop waiting for tomorrow, live life to the full today!** Become disciplined in taking captive impure and selfish thoughts, stop that romantic fantasy in its tracks and pray for that gorgeous guy/girl instead!
- **We are all sexual beings, but no marriage for the Christian means no sex.** Channelling sexual energy into other streams allows us to be fulfilled individuals in control of our passions rather than controlled by them.
- **Prayerfully commit your life to God, not just once, but repeatedly**. He is in control and can be trusted with our anxieties, futures and dreams.

Becky Brain
wrote as a CMF Staffworker and GP trainee

LINKS *Nucleus*, January 2003. www.cmf.org.uk/publications/content.asp?context=article&id=347

A **female doctor writes...** I have always struggled with being single and the pursuit of an 'other half' led me to date some very unsuitable men. I longed to find a decent 'Christian man' but had little success. All my friends were getting married and having kids. I remember God saying to me 'How could anyone love you more than I do?' This was a comfort initially but went out of the window when the next non-Christian guy showed me interest. I went from partner to partner totally addicted to the thrill of the chase and the feeling of being wanted. I sinned sexually, was conned out of my savings by one partner and cheated on. I was devastated. After my 'behaviour' I doubted God would ever honour my desire for a decent Christian partner. He did, and I am now going out with a great guy who accepts the struggles of my past.

One with God is a majority.
Billy Graham

Philippians 4:11 **I am not saying this because I am in need, for I have learned to be content whatever the circumstances.**

A **male doctor writes...** It can be difficult to meet fellow Christians: shift work will take you out of many church events and you will no longer be part of the Christian societies you joined at university. You may continue being single for a few more years. But you will be surrounded by many bright, attractive, young colleagues, who will be 'out of bounds' when it comes to relationships. Coupled with the large proportion of time juniors spend with each other this means it can be very challenging being single.

Not having a spouse or children means that you will still have lots of free time to do things you enjoy (and the money to do it!) Without intentionally booking in fun activities and holidays with friends, loneliness can creep up on you, which makes resisting temptation far harder. Instead of moping I learnt to enjoy my singleness and live counter-culture to a society that puts pressure on you to couple up.

think it over...

1 If you are single, is loneliness a problem? What can you do practically to prevent this?

2 If you are married or in a relationship, what do you do to make sure single people are supported in your church?

3 Do you have strong and accountable relationships with other believers? If single, will these continue into marriage? If not, how might you establish them?

TAKE HOME MESSAGE: **The main challenge when single is to live for God today**

Today is the tomorrow we worried about yesterday.

stress + burnout

Emotional breakdown never arises out of the blue. There is always a background to it and usually there are warning signs that, if heeded, might prevent a precipitous grind to a halt.

Understanding that certain personality traits common amongst doctors can lead to anxiety and stress-related illness is vital if we are to take preventive action at an early stage. The trick is to recognise the early warning signs.

- **Increasing irritability** – little things make you lose your temper.
- **Paranoia** – supportive colleagues seem to have changed.
- **Dread** – the journey to work and/or home is filled with a sense of dread.
- **Enemies at the gate** – nice patients suddenly become demanding, selfish time-wasters!
- **Night terrors** – you find it difficult to sleep well, if at all.
- **Increasing isolation** – people tend to avoid you.
- **Vanishing pleasure domes** – things you usually love just don't give you a buzz anymore.

Turning points

Why is it that we doctors are so reluctant to accept help when we need it, especially perhaps when it comes to other healthcare providers delivering it? Pride is almost certainly to blame. Breakdown is a form of regression – of emotional shut down to enable us to survive. In coming out on the other side, it is often necessary to relearn basic principles. Nearly all of the important ones are mentioned in Scripture. Rightly understood and applied these can both bring about and maintain emotional recovery and healing.

Trevor Stammers wrote as a GP and lecturer in medical ethics

An offer you can't refuse?

Some sayings of Jesus seem to pile on the pressure: 'Whoever forces you to go one mile, go with him two'. However, there are occasions when it is not only right but necessary to say 'No'. James implies this when he says that our 'No' should be a plain 'No'. We do not have to get frustrated or always give an explanation. Sometimes we do have to turn down requests to do things. We must beware the tyranny of uncommanded work, since God only promises to equip us in every good thing 'to do his will', not everything others demand of us.

Dialogue of the deaf

Those around us often see the early signs of burnout long before we do. After I had ground to a halt, my partners all spoke about having noticed things such as uncharacteristic irritability and undue haste many months previously. They had been reluctant to say anything though as, sadly, the teachable spirit that marks the truly wise is not one of my outstanding traits.

God of the grey

Sometimes we can become fixed on a false understanding of Jesus being the answer to all our needs. Yet, sometimes there are no answers this side of heaven. As doctors, we usually like things to be precise and clear. We find uncertainty stressful. In this broken world, where many things are not black and white, we need to discover that the Lord is also 'God of the grey'.

Being a Christian is all about being vulnerable. However, it is also about being certain of what we as yet hope for. God puts his treasure in us, weak and earthen vessels that easily crack, so that the glory might go to him.

Triple Helix, Summer 2007. www.cmf.org.uk/publications/content.asp?context=article&id=1949

testimony

Gareth says... the worst thing about being stressed is that you never realise how stressed you are until the stress finishes. I thought I coped well under pressure during my medical SHO jobs and tried to cope with prayer, exercise and distraction outside work. I know these carried me through a stressful time, but sometime you have to accept that you need to change specialty. God has been faithful and provided a job in an unglamorous specialty I would never have considered whilst at medical school. My stress levels and health have improved dramatically.

Sarah says... As I worked a non-compliant rota with a seemingly insurmountable workload, feeling completely out of my depth, I was encouraged by two biblical truths. God is with us in every situation and he will give us the strength and the energy to go on (Isaiah 40:28-31). We are not working to impress our seniors and to meet their expectations: 'It is the Lord Christ you are serving.' (Colossians 3:23-24)

It's when I'm stressed that I am least likely to do things that will help me to de-stress. I have realised the importance of taking time out to get something to eat and drink – even on the busiest of shifts; to talk and pray things through with a friend; and to seek support from a senior colleague before things spiral out of control.

Worry often gives a small thing a big shadow.

Mark 1:35 **Very early in the morning, while it was still dark, Jesus got up, left the house and went off to a solitary place, where he prayed.**

think it over...

Mark up a **large 3x3 noughts and crosses grid**.
Then, carry out each step in turn without looking at the following steps beforehand. Each step is best done rapidly and without too much thought.

Enter into the boxes the nine major areas of life that take up most of your time.

Below each entry, put an approximate percentage of your time taken up by that activity.

Add up the total of the nine percentages you have entered.

Trevor Stammers says: If you have a total percentage exceeding 100, you may want to consider the need for a lifestyle adjustment. Interestingly, many people find that they forget to mark sleeping or eating into their grids. Prayer, time with family and sex are also commonly omitted. My personal percentage at crisis point was 206!

TAKE HOME MESSAGE: **Watch for signs of burnout, and seek help early!**

exam revision

For medics, exams are an ever present feature of life – and yet they don't get any less stressful. Is there anything we can do about this?

1. Plan your revision

Whilst at junior school I had a brief encounter with rugby in the 3rd XV. We won four of our six matches, due more to youthful energy and enthusiasm than sound tactics. I remember being amazed by one of the teams we lost to. We played as 15 individuals but they played as one team. At each set-piece the whole team knew what they were going to do. They had a game plan. And they won because of it.

When it comes to exam revision most of us are a bit like my rugby team was – we tend to leave things to chance. We might work hard but rarely do we plan ahead and if we do, we make an unrealistic timetable that a 'Brain of Britain' would find it hard to keep. If we want to succeed we need to have a revision game plan.

2. Plan rest periods

When God made us he didn't make us to work seven days a week. He made us as finite beings so that we would need to take at least one day a week to rest and remember our relationship with him. What wonderful news! God wants us to take sufficient time to rest. He doesn't want us to wear ourselves out working all hours of the day and night.

If we take proper rest periods we will find that our work efficiency increases rather than reduces. We end up being able to do more work rather than less.

Jim Paul wrote as a palliative care trainee

3. Choose your friends

Beware the friends who increase your stress levels by testing your knowledge on a topic that they have just revised! Avoid friends who waste your time by complaining how stressed they are or who encourage you in fruitless activity and procrastination.

Instead look for a friend who will revise with you and encourage you to keep going. One excellent friend who is 'outside medicine' is Jesus. He said that he will send to each person who loves him his Spirit who will help restore our peace by reminding us that he is the true Lord of our lives, including our exams.

medicine is not the be all and end all of life

4. Keep things in perspective

When your mind is focused on exams it's easy to get life out of perspective. Passing or failing the exam becomes our whole world and revision a never-ending state of limbo. Failing exams becomes the worst event we can imagine and this fear multiplies our stress levels until they become a panic.

Despite what our professors teach us, medicine is not the be all and end all of life. I don't think that it's God's number one priority either. Our relationships with other people and above all with our heavenly Father should have more priority than our careers.

LINKS *Nucleus, April 1999. www.cmf.org.uk/publications/content.asp?context=article&id=713*

Unlike at medical school, it is very common to need more than one attempt

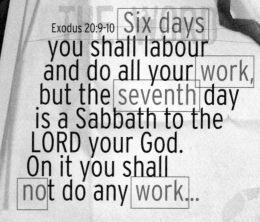

Relationships should have priority

testimony

Gareth says... I failed my MRCP Part 1 three times. Finding time to do good study was the hardest part of being a junior – the hours were long, and studying when tired is a pointless activity. I found that going to the hospital library an hour before work gave me the opportunity to study when fresh and without interruption. The other thing I eventually learnt was to catch up on sleep before the exams. When I finally did pass I made sure I was getting ready for bed at 9:45 every night of the week before the exams. This meant that I was fresh and better able to cope with answering the questions, and I am sure it made all the difference.

Russell says... I found revising for my MRCGP quite different to revision at medical school. There weren't nearly so many friends around to help – I lived nowhere near the others taking the exam on my training scheme. Money was an added pressure to pass first time – in all I spent about £3,000 on exam fees, courses and postgraduate certification that year.
   A big help was a course at the start of my revision rather than at the last minute, meaning that I directed my work more productively. I also really benefitted from ensuring that I did very little work at all in the 24 hours before the exam. It was far more important to be awake and alert on the day than to remember one or two last minute facts that probably won't come up anyway!

Exodus 20:9-10 **Six days you shall labour and do all your work, but the seventh day is a Sabbath to the LORD your God. On it you shall not do any work...**

think it over...

1 Do I have clear plans for revision for upcoming exams?

2 What can I do to ensure I take time off each week?

3 What is the worst that will happen if I fail a particular exam?

4 Pray that God will help you get your career priorities in perspective

TAKE HOME MESSAGE: **Keep study stress in perspective and focus on Jesus**

Clocks slay time... time is dead as long as it is being clicked off by little wheels; only when the clock stops does time come to life.
William Faulkner

time

Jesus uniquely maintained a balance between worship, prayer, family, friends, work and rest. To do this, he kept an intimate relationship with God and he had a clear view of his life task; he is our model.

Jesus guarded his devotional life – He regularly spent time in prayer and in studying the Scriptures, especially during periods of intense activity (Luke 5:15-16). He was immersed in the Word of God. Be readers and students of the Bible – make it one of your first priorities.

Jesus did not sin – Sin weakens our witness more than anything else; it consumes our energies and our thoughts. We need to be clean right through. By cutting wrong thoughts and behaviours out of our lives, we have more time and energy to be used by God (2 Timothy 2:20-21).

Everyone had their own agenda for Jesus. Despite this pressure, **Jesus did not let demands from others control how he spent his time** – nor was he put off by criticism and threats. We need to remember who we are actually serving. Jesus ultimately dictates the terms. His will takes priority and at times this means making choices that those around us may not understand or respect (Mark 3:31-34).

Jesus had a clear strategy – We find Jesus' mission statement in his sermon to his own community at Nazareth: 'The Spirit of the Lord is on me, because he has anointed me to preach good news to the poor. He has sent me to proclaim freedom for the prisoners and recovery of sight for the blind, to release the oppressed, to proclaim the year of the Lord's favour.' (Luke 4:18-19) We need to have an overall purpose and vision in line with our own calling within the body of Christ. We have to take control of our lives by choosing to obey God in the same way Jesus did.

Jesus fulfilled everything in his mission statement, but he had a priority – the preaching of the gospel – which took precedence over all his other ministries (Luke 4:42-43). There are many orders of priority given in the Bible, such as the gospel having priority over healing. For each of us, the priorities will be different but there are certain activities and people God wants us to prioritise.

Jesus made time for individuals – In the midst of Jesus' busy ministry, he did not let the urgent (but less important) crowd out the important (but less urgent). Jesus was on the way to see someone who was critically ill with an acute infection, and he was stopped by a woman with long-standing menorrhagia. She got his full attention and then, as if to vindicate his decision, God enabled him to raise Jairus' daughter from the dead (Luke 8:40-56). In your ministry as doctors, you will not be able to spend time with everybody. Pray that God will show you the people that he wants you to pause with.

Procrastination can be costly, so it is important not to make it a habit

Jesus' strategy was not to do all the work himself but to equip others. This can be particularly hard for us in the medical profession. Many of us are independent pioneers and loners; but God wants us to equip others to do our work so that the work multiplies. We may find that those we equip end up doing a far better job than we did (Matthew 9:37-38).

Jesus chose his company – We become like those we choose to spend our time with. How many of the men and women God used in biblical history spent a period of their lives as understudy to some role model? Think of Joshua and Moses, Elisha and Elijah, or Timothy and Paul. Latch

Peter Saunders wrote as CMF General Secretary

testimony

Use your time to honour God

Elizabeth writes... My first weekend ward cover as a junior doctor was horrible. On my own on the wards, I had no idea how to prioritise jobs! Extremely stressed, I did each job as it came – not finding time to go to the loo, let alone to eat! At 3 pm, due to finish but half-way through my jobs, I felt unable to hand it all over. By 4.30 pm I was in a state and burst into tears in front of a disgruntled patient! I then realised that not stopping had made me less efficient and went to eat. I finished at 8 pm having learned two important lessons:

- Time management includes taking time to eat and drink! A 15 minute rest makes me more efficient
- Time management involves being willing to hand things over and being honest when struggling. Keeping calm and avoiding 'hypoglycaemia' are important skills for a junior doctor!

Psalm 139:16 **All the days ordained for me were written in your book before one of them came to be.**

on to those older Christians you can really learn from. Seek to learn what it is that makes them effective in God's service and emulate it.

Jesus realised it was important to withdraw and rest – even in the face of pressing need. We also need to take time out from work and ministry at regular intervals. Burnout is a major problem for Christian doctors who are motivated by a strong sense of responsibility and who are aware of the vast amount of unmet need.

Jesus was never idle – or slothful. Hard work brings God glory because in working hard we are emulating God who himself works. It's important that we think of all service to God as work, not just paid employment. Spending time with our families and friends is just as much work in God's service. There is no-one apart from you who can be a husband to your wife, a wife to your husband, a parent to your children or a child to your parents.

My prayer is that we would learn from Jesus to use our time in a way that most glorifies God. But don't let worries about time management consume you. Trust God, for his grace is all sufficient; his Spirit lives and works in you.

think it over...

1 When are the times of day that you concentrate best? How do you make the most of these?

2 Do you have an overall purpose and strategy like Jesus did? When did you last review it?

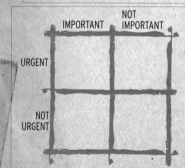

Fill in the box with the things you need to do today. Do now anything in the top-left box; schedule anything in the top-right; see if you could delegate things in the bottom left. If it's in the bottom right box, does anyone need to do it at all?

27

unemployment

It's a recession when your neighbour loses his job;
it's a depression when you lose your own.
— Harry S Truman

Unemployment now faces junior doctors because of increasing competition for training posts. Doctors from outside the EU require a permit to work in the UK, and fewer jobs are available for newly qualified GPs. As Christian doctors, our hope lies in the Lord, but how does that translate when the rubber hits the road? Two doctors share their experiences of unemployment.

Victoria writes... I was born and grew up in Uzbekistan, of Korean ethnicity. I became a Christian because I always believed there was more to life than 'this big Universe'.

After graduation, I entered a cardiology residency. I dreamed of training in interventional cardiology. I felt that a placement in the UK could give me the experience I needed, and started preparing for the PLAB exam to enable me to practise in the UK. By God's mercy I passed it on the first attempt. It was then I faced unemployment. I received no reply from the dozens of applications I submitted throughout the UK.

While in this trial, God provided me with a local Christian couple who became my 'English parents'. They provided me with advice, support and prayer. He also provided me with Christian friends and timely clinical attachments. At times of utter despair, I relied on his word. I meditated regularly on verses such as: 'Seek first his kingdom and his righteousness, and all these things will be given to you as well'. (Matthew 6:33)

My other problem was my identity. I realised that much of my identity had been tied up in what I was doing. I became sharply aware that I had no answer to the question that everybody asks on introductions – namely 'What do you do?' I was unemployed from December 2004 until February 2007. During that time I prepared for exams, continued in my clinical attachments, and worked as an honorary clinical fellow.

You might wonder what happened next. I persevered and secured a place as a part-time maternity locum. I then worked my way through various SHO positions before stepping up as an acting respiratory specialist registrar. With God's help, I completed my MRCP exam and am now working as a respiratory registrar. Slowly but surely, God made a way for me at his pace. Through my experiences, I learnt that God is good all the time and working for the good of those who love him (Romans 8:28). My identity lies within him rather than in my status as a doctor, and through his grace I can now identify with those who also are going through unemployment.

Elizabeth writes... As I approached the end of my registrar year, I started to become increasingly anxious about finding a job. The rumour mill was flooded with stories of newly qualified GPs being out of work and having to survive on the 'hand to mouth' existence of locum work. This didn't bother me initially, but then stories began to abound about the locum market being flooded and there being little opportunity for career progression.

I decided to send a copy of my CV to every practice in the PCT explaining that I was looking for work. By 'pure chance' I received a call from a practice about a salaried position they were about to advertise. They needed somebody with some surgical experience and felt that I would be ideal. I went to the interview and was offered the job. Initially it was a six-month contract but I was told in all likelihood it would be a permanent post.

I must stress that all this job-seeking was done largely without God's guidance. Yes, I read the Bible and prayed regularly but I felt that I didn't

Victoria Kim wrote as a respiratory registrar, and **Elizabeth Croton** as a GP

LINKS *Triple Helix, Easter 2010; www.cmf.org.uk/publications/content.asp?context=article&id=25513*

The hardest work in the world is being out of work
— Whitney Young Jr

Job insecurity is a global issue

Romans 8:28 And we know that in all things God works for the good of those who love him.

have time to 'wait for the Lord' (Psalm 27:14). I had been there four months when I discovered that another salaried GP appointed before me was not having her contract renewed, for 'financial reasons'. Shortly afterwards I was told the same. I had just over a month to find myself another job.

This was a real blow to my confidence and I became increasingly anxious regarding my future. Like Victoria, I meditated on the Bible and tried to convince myself that God was working for my good through all this (Romans 8:28). I also dreaded people asking me about how my career was going. My identity had been centred on my status for so long and now this was stripped away from me.

I was forced to turn to the Lord and cling to him instead: 'But now, Lord, what do I look for? My hope is in you'. (Psalm 39:7)

I became extremely envious of those GPs who had secure jobs because I felt they were better than me. I also began to worry about money – not because I was in debt but because I wanted the security of knowing I had a regular income. I didn't trust that the Lord would provide for me. I managed through locum work to keep afloat for the next four months. The Lord had taught me a valuable lesson regarding submission and obedience and I tried to walk closely with him through praying and reading his Word. Again 'by chance' I was approached by a practice who had received my CV and I now work on a permanent basis for them. I realise the Lord did provide but this is not the main moral of the story for me. As Christian doctors, our identity is in Christ, not our degrees and for me it took the loss of my regular work to realise this. I won't ever forget this lesson though.

think it over...

1 Many doctors assume that they will never be short of work. What is the job situation in your specialty at the moment?

2 How do you answer the question 'What do you do?' Is your answer purely about medicine?

3 What steps might you take to ensure medicine doesn't take over your identity?

TAKE HOME MESSAGE: **Our identity is in Christ, not in our medical work**

Why do bioethics Matter?

I n my second year at medical school we were given a series of ethics lectures. These were delivered by a variety of academics, many of whom were eminent in their field. However, despite this and the exam at the end of the course, most of my colleagues couldn't see why the subject might be relevant to their future practice and almost no-one turned up.

Four or five years down the line, now I've started working, I sense there's even more reluctance to think about ethical issues. Within the NHS there seems to be an endemic culture where many of my colleagues get on with their day to day job, almost in a little bubble, and don't stop to challenge or even reflect on the problems facing their profession.

Bioethics without doctors?

Bioethics, the area of study that looks at complex healthcare dilemmas, first emerged in the United States in the 1970s. Previously, whatever the doctor said went, and the patient had little say in the matter. However, times thankfully changed and doctors began to realise the importance of involving their patients in decision-making.

Things have gone to the other extreme though, and doctors seem to have been almost completely pushed out of academic ethical discussions, in favour of philosophers, lawyers and theologians.

Bioethics without Christians?

Helen Barratt wrote as an FY1 doctor

At the same time as doctors have been pushed out of ethical debate, there has been a rather more concerted effort to push religious perspectives – particularly those of Christians – out of the arena as well.

Society has little time for religion as a source of ethical norms. However, in his book *Matters of Life and Death*, Professor John Wyatt argues that we must defend a Christian point of view for three reasons: first, because it is true – the Christian worldview fits with reality, the way the world is made! Secondly, it also works and leads to beneficial consequences for the whole community. Finally, our perspective as Christians about what is right and wrong more often than not fits with the basic intuitions of the human heart.

The Christian worldview fits with reality

Bioethics needs Christians

As Christians, we have a responsibility to be looking forward, proclaiming and predicting according to God's Word, communicating clearly the potential consequences of developments in medicine. The New Testament writer James says 'Anyone, then, who knows the good he ought to do and doesn't do it, sins' (James 4:17).

Many ethical issues (such as euthanasia and our increasingly pro-death culture) simply reflect a much greater problem – that society has rejected Christian faith and values. As well as seeking to influence the medical profession, we also have a responsibility to convey the wider hope we have as Christians and this is something the world desperately needs to hear: by God's grace, we know that our present sufferings are limited, and that we are ultimately assured of eternal life, as well as freedom from pain and the burden of a frail body.

01

Ethical issues: they touch us at the core of our being.
John Wyatt

testimony

Helen's experience... In my final year at medical school, I undertook a split elective. For half the time I was completing research for a bioethics degree, looking at human enhancement technologies in the light of biblical anthropology. For the rest of the time, I was based in a critical care environment where questions arose in my mind on a regular basis about the use of technology at the limits of medicine and how this applied to the patient being subjected to it. One humbling – and unexpected – benefit of the whole elective was the realisation that the debates about ethics and medicine (however far-fetched) could, and should, never be simply academic exercises. The patients and relatives in that unit didn't care about slippery slopes, autonomy or any of the other 'four principles', nor for that matter about the application of Old Testament scripture and the interpretation of early Christian writings.

   Your friends and relatives will respect your opinion as a medic. I can think of several situations where non-Christian friends collared me, knowing my interest in ethics, and asked for my opinion on, for example, IVF. Although this is a huge topic, which can't easily be covered in a brief conversation, such discussions have presented me with fantastic opportunities to talk about Christian principles and my faith more generally. Beware however that this sort of question may reflect a huge personal struggle or pain, as I discovered with one friend, so must be handled with sensitivity – another lesson in taking ethics beyond academic debate.

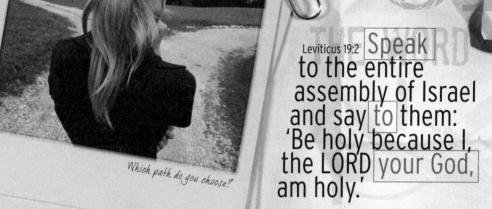

Which path do you choose?

Leviticus 19:2 Speak to the entire assembly of Israel and say to them: 'Be holy because I, the LORD your God, am holy.'

think it over...

1 When did you last have a conversation at work about an ethical issue?

2 Can you think of opportunities to raise ethical issues during your day to day work?

3 What are the common ethical issues in your specialty? Could you explain a Christian viewpoint on them if asked?

TAKE HOME MESSAGE: **Ethics is just as much a part of day to day practice as an ECG**

33

Authority of the Bible

Following Christ involves following his commands. The law of Christ referred to in John 13:34-35, 1 Corinthians 9:21 and Galatians 6:2 involves bearing one another's burdens, loving each other as he has loved us. These verses summarise beautifully the substance of Jesus' teaching, but we cannot conclude that the rest of Scripture is unnecessary. Jesus expands this core of moral teaching throughout the Gospels, particularly in the Sermon on the Mount (Matthew 5-7), but he also endorses the whole Bible.

Jesus and the Old Testament

Jesus put his stamp of authority on the Old Testament. He treated its historical narratives as fact (eg Matthew 16:4). He repeatedly quoted it as the final court of appeal in debates (Matthew 4:1-11). He believed its prophecies were fulfilled in him (Luke 24:44, John 4:25-26) and he obeyed its ethical teaching (Matthew 5:17-21, 23:23).

Jesus commanded his disciples to obey the teachers of the law in so far as they were faithful to the Law of Moses (Matthew 23:2-3), and said that anyone who broke one of the least of the Law's commandments and taught others to do the same would be called least in the Kingdom of Heaven. His disciples are expected to go beyond mere observance of the letter of the Law to fulfilment of the very principle of love upon which it is based (Matthew 5:17-20).

Jesus and the New Testament

Jesus commissioned the New Testament. We can be confident that the Apostles recorded what Christ said (Luke 1:3), because he personally commissioned them and gave them the authority to teach in his name (Matthew 28:19-20). Christ's own testimony was that he would enable them by means of his Holy Spirit (John 14:25-26) to 'teach them all things', 'remind them of everything he said', 'take what was his and make it known to them' and 'guide them into all truth' (John 16:12-15).

True, we are now 'not under law but under grace' (Romans 6:14) but this refers to the basis of our justification rather than our ethical obligations. Under the New Covenant, God's laws are written on our hearts (Jeremiah 31:33) and we are now enabled and exhorted to live 'according to the Spirit' (Galatians 5:22-26). While our righteousness is 'by faith' (Romans 1:17), the evidence of the genuineness of our faith is that we perform good works (James 2:26) by being conformed to Jesus Christ.

The sufficiency of the Bible

The Bible is sufficient (2 Timothy 3:16-17) and contains stern warnings about adding to or subtracting from it (Revelation 22:18-19). We should share Jesus' own high regard for Scripture, and regularly hear, read, study and meditate on it. Still, we must be careful not to fall into one of three traps.

Antinomianism dispenses with law altogether. The antinomian argues that since we are under grace, and not law, and since the death of Christ cleanses us from all unrighteousness, we are no longer under any obligation to obey the moral law. This flies in the face of Paul's own rhetorical question, 'Shall we sin because we are not under law but under grace?' to which he supplies his own answer 'By no means!' and goes on to point out that our freedom from the condemnation of the law means that we are now 'slaves of righteousness' and thereby obliged to obey God's commands (Romans 6:15-18).

Peter Saunders
wrote as General
Secretary of CMF

LINKS Turning the Tide. www.cmf.org.uk/publications/content.asp?context=article&id=1334

02

The Bible: ...the most valuable thing that this world affords. The Coronation Service

Jesus endorses the whole Bible

2 Timothy 3:16-17 **All** Scripture is God-breathed and is useful for teaching, rebuking, correcting and training in righteousness, so that the man of God may be thoroughly equipped for every good work.

Situationism retains the law but claims that in certain situations the commandments may be suspended in favour of the higher principle of 'love to one's neighbour' (Matthew 22:39-40). The situationist argues that one may intentionally kill in certain situations and yet be acting 'in love'. This contravenes Christ's own teaching that obedience to the greater commandments of the law does not in any way excuse disobedience to the lesser (Matthew 5:17-20, 23:23). It also begs the question of what a 'loving' action is (Deuteronomy 12:8). This has tremendous dangers.

Legalism substitutes human oral tradition for God's law and introduces a non-biblical hierarchy of sins (Mark 7:8-13). God's true commandments are distorted such that they become impractical and in fact impossible for all but a select group to obey. Thus the prohibition against 'intentional killing of the innocent' may become a directive to 'strive officiously to sustain life at all costs'. The result is that the most important principles of love, justice and mercy are ultimately lost sight of and a new law is imposed (Matthew 23:23). A tragic consequence can be that, in the case of terminal care, the attainable goals of caring, consoling and comforting are forgotten as the doctor, driven more by guilt than compassion, feels he must do everything technologically possible to prolong the patient's life.

All these heresies are over-reactions to mistakes of the past: antinomianism to joyless obedience, situationism to obedience without compassion, and legalism to lawless indulgence. The best argument against them is the practical demonstration of joyful, compassionate, obedient Christian service.

think it over...

1 Which parts of the Bible's teaching are you least comfortable with?

2 How high is your regard for Scripture?

3 Have you ever heard situationist arguments as justification for Christians supporting abortion and assisted suicide?

4 How could you respond to these arguments?

Ethical principles from the bible

We should resist the temptation to construct a pharisaical list of do's and don'ts but rather look for biblical ethical principles to guide our decision making. These can be summed up in the commandments to 'love God with all our heart, soul and mind' and 'to love our neighbour as ourselves' (Matthew 22:37-40). While respecting the Ten Commandments, we should recognise that true Christian morality involves going beyond the mere letter of the law (Matthew 5:21-22, 27-28) to the very spirit of love on which it is based (1 Corinthians 13:4-8). The following principles are based on the Ten Commandments (Exodus 20:3-17).

1. The sovereignty of God – You shall have no other gods before me
God is the Creator (Genesis 1:1), the Sustainer (Hebrews 1:3) and the Lord of all life. He is also absolute arbiter of right and wrong and has spoken clearly in history through his word and through his Son Jesus Christ (Hebrews 1:1-2), in whom all his fullness dwells (Colossians 1:19). We must always put him first.

2. Stewardship – You shall not make for yourself an idol
God has made us stewards of his creation and guardians of the planet (Genesis 1:26,28). This validates scientific enquiry and application but is not a licence for exploitation, nor for seeing medicine rather than God as mankind's saviour. We must always exercise our delegated authority for good, especially for individual human beings. Furthermore we should do it according to God's revealed standards of right and wrong. The end does not justify the means (Romans 3:8).

Peter Saunders
wrote as General Secretary of CMF

3. Honouring God's character – You shall not misuse the name of the Lord your God
We must recognise and acknowledge God as the real source of all good gifts (James 1:17; 1 Corinthians 4:7), upholding his compassion, grace, patience, love, faithfulness, forgiveness and justice (Exodus 34:6,7); and not bringing dishonour to his name in our words or actions; nor should we seek glory for ourselves.

4. Work and rest – Remember the Sabbath Day... six days shall you labour
We have an obligation to work (2 Thessalonians 3:10-13), to serve others in order to provide for our own needs and those of our family (1 Timothy 5:8) and to imitate God who is himself a worker. But we must also honour and recommend the Creator's rule of one day's rest in seven, recognising that it was made for our pleasure and benefit (Isaiah 58:13-14; Mark 2:27) and as a sign of the rest to come (Hebrews 4:9-11).

All human life is made in God's image and is worthy of respect

5. Authority and the family – Honour your father and your mother
God has established human authorities as his agents to serve and protect us and we should submit to them and not rebel (Romans 13:1-7). Most important among these is the family which is God's provision for the protection, nurture and discipline of children (Deuteronomy 6:6,7; Ephesians 6:1-4) and the stability of society as a whole.

6. The sanctity of life – You shall not murder
All human life is made in God's image (Genesis 9:5,6) and is worthy of the utmost respect from its beginning to end. This includes the unborn (Psalm 139:13-16; Isaiah 49:1; Job 10:8-9), and people who are disabled (Leviticus 19:14), vulnerable (Exodus 22:21-24) or advanced in age (Leviticus 19:32). The heart of Christianity is that we must love as Christ himself loved

LINKS *Turning the Tide. www.cmf.org.uk/publications/content.asp?context=article&id=1330*

...in a world of violence and oppression we are called to compassionate service to the poor and deprived.
Bruce Nicholls

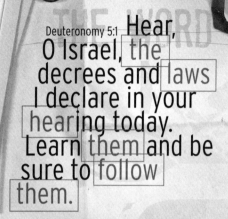

The grace and mercy of the cross wins every time

Deuteronomy 5:1 Hear, O Israel, the decrees and laws I declare in your hearing today. Learn them and be sure to follow them.

(John 13:34), that the strong lay down their lives for the weak (Philippians 2:5-8, Romans 5:6-8).

7. Sexuality and Marriage – You shall not commit adultery

Marriage is a life-long, publicly recognised, heterosexual, monogamous relationship (Genesis 2:24; Matthew 19:4-6; Ephesians 5:31-33) and is representative of Christ's own relationship with the church. Sex is God's good gift for intimacy (Matthew 19:4), pleasure (Proverbs 5:18,19) and procreation (Genesis 1:28) but must only take place within marriage.

8. Respect for property – You shall not steal

God has blessed human beings materially in order that they may provide for their own needs and those of others (2 Corinthians 9:8). We should show respect for the property of others and seek to use what he has given us in accordance with his revealed will.

9. Veracity – You shall not give false testimony

We should 'speak the truth in love' (Ephesians 4:15) at all times, using words to build others up not tear them down. Lying through commission or omission runs counter to the nature of God himself (Numbers 23:19) and leads to injustice. We should be people of our word (James 5:12).

10. Contentment – You shall not covet...

We should be grateful and content with what God gives us (Philippians 4:11-12), not being driven by jealousy or desire for the possessions, relationships, gifts or honour of others. Rather we should desire to do his will, to have his gifts to serve others (1 Corinthians 12:31) and most of all to desire God himself (Psalm 37:4), knowing that he will provide us with what we need.

think it over...

1 Wouldn't it just be easier if the Bible were a list of 'do's and don'ts'?

2 Think through how each of the 10 principles above would affect the care of:

a) An alcoholic who presents to A&E in liver failure

b) A 15 year old girl in general practice requesting an abortion

c) A 34 year old man in prison for burglary who says he has lost the painkillers given last week

37

The rise of designer babies and parental selection for specific traits raises a host of bioethical and legal issues that will dominate reproductive rights debates in the 21st century.

Antenatal Screening

You are working for a consultant obstetrician who is very keen on his patients undergoing as much antenatal screening as possible. He is not in favour of abortion for social reasons but justifies them entirely for fetal abnormality, saying, 'Don't you believe it's a parental right to have a normal baby?' How would you defend your unborn neighbour in such a discussion?

There are two important keys to handling this situation. First, you must think carefully about how to respond – what angle is this doctor coming from? Second, you are working for him so this could be an ongoing discussion that does not require you to demolish all his arguments in one sitting.

Eugenics by the back door

In a politically correct society, a safe starting point for debate is the issue of discrimination. Verbally or physically abusing a fellow human being on the grounds of gender, race, sexuality or beliefs is illegal. However, in the clean, sanitised precincts of the antenatal clinic (ANC), worse thoughts and actions are encouraged.

Mothers-to-be are commenced on a conveyor belt of blood tests, scans and sometimes amniocentesis (which itself carries a 1% miscarriage risk!) to check that 'baby is OK'. But do these women really understand the implications? Is truly informed consent obtained for this screening process, where abortion is often the only 'therapy'? Only the boldest couples will actually refuse the tests on the basis that they've thought it through and will unconditionally accept whatever child is born to them. The complex and expensive tests that are offered in the ANC amount to one of the most expensive eugenics projects the world has ever seen. The government does not spend millions of pounds of taxpayers' money on tests for Down's syndrome just so mothers can

John Wenham
wrote as a GP

be 'prepared before the child is born'. There is a strong drive to reduce the 'financial burden' on society of caring for these people by aborting them.

Protecting the weak

But, wait a minute! Isn't the medical profession supposed to be a caring profession? Or are we free to decide when caring comes at too high a price? The law exists to protect the rights of the weak. Doctors are trained to look after the vulnerable. Parents have a duty to care for their children. The 1967 Abortion Act turned these three historic guiding principles on their head and made the womb a pretty dangerous place to be.

Social abortion supports a woman's choice over the baby's right to be cared for. The process is indiscriminate unless a GP or gynaecologist challenges their wishes. Abortion for fetal abnormality is, because of the discrimination involved, in some senses a worse act.

A right to be 'normal'?

What constitutes a normal baby and in what circumstances does he consider there to be 'a substantial risk of serious handicap' justifying abortion? This is a very grey area but he must have some standards that he lives by, which may give you further opportunity for discussion.

How does he balance his obstetric responsibility to protect and deliver a baby safely with a parental right to a normal baby? Does he believe the Darwinian principle that only the fittest should survive? That surely is a flawed argument given that Darwin suggested a theory for evolution; he was not recommending that humans forcibly remove the weaker members from society. If we argue that a normal baby is a parental right, how long before we decide normal is an IQ of >130, blue eyes, blonde hair and a physique to die for?

Nucleus, July 2005. www.cmf.org.uk/publications/content.asp?context=article&id=1632

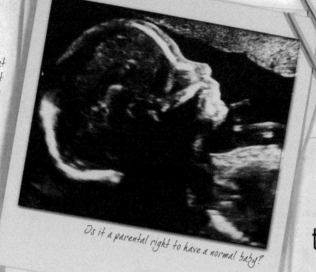
Is it a parental right to have a normal baby?

04

> *The Christian in medicine, conscious of the Great Physician, has an ultimate touchstone to apply. What decision should I take in this problem, which I can present to God as work performed on his behalf?*
> *Rex Gardner*

testimony

Kevin says... Any in-depth discussion is a challenge in a busy antenatal clinic where 50 or more women may need to be seen in a three hour period. For many junior doctors in obstetrics, discussion of antenatal screening is limited to a simple 'we usually do these tests' – if it happens at all. As an obstetric SHO I tried to discuss these further – not always easy when working in an area where many patients spoke limited English. Even with these constraints, a surprising number of patients didn't want a test that could only result in an abortion – when they realised that they had a choice.

Most consultants took little interest in what we actually said so long as we saw the patients quickly and kept good notes, so I had reasonable freedom in what I did – but I was aware that my actions sometimes caused patients to receive mixed messages when they had been seen by midwives who often enthusiastically advocated every test on offer.

The small amount that you can do as a junior doctor is well worth it, but ultimately a change in society's attitude to disability - a recognition that there is no 'right' to a 'perfect baby' - is needed.

Psalm 41:1 **Blessed is he who has regard for the weak; the LORD delivers him in times of trouble.**

think it over...

1 Do you think there is a 'right to a perfect baby'? Would your non-Christian colleagues agree with you?

2 How can you ensure that women are given an informed choice about antenatal screening?

3 What can we do practically to alter society's attitude towards the disabled?

TAKE HOME MESSAGE: **Discrimination against the weak isn't always easy to spot - look out for it!**

think... about the beginning of life...

Consequences of abortion

The total number of abortions in the UK continues to rise. Almost one in four pregnancies in England ends in abortion, and it is widely acknowledged that one woman in three in England now has an abortion at some point. In the last few years there has been growing awareness of long term complications.

Preterm delivery

The RCOG's 2004 guidance states that 'abortion may be associated with a small increase in the risk of subsequent miscarriage or preterm delivery'. Many recent and methodologically robust studies give cause for greater concern than the RCOG's guidance suggests.

Thorp *et al* published a detailed review in 2003. They had analysed results for 24 published studies and reported that twelve found a positive association between abortion and subsequent preterm delivery. Seven published studies found a 'dose-response' effect: the more induced abortions there had been, the more the risk estimate increased.

This association is further supported by two more recent European studies (EPIPAGE and EUROPOP). The link is significant for health outcomes in subsequent pregnancies, with all that means for the couple involved and for their baby, but it is also very significant in terms of economic costs for the family, for the National Health Service, and for society.

Peter Saunders wrote as General Secretary of CMF and **Andrew Fergusson** wrote as CMF Head of Communications

Consequences for mental health

Since 2000, there has been much evidence from around the world in robust and methodologically sound controlled studies that abortion causes increased psychiatric hospitalisation and outpatient attendance, increased substance abuse during subsequent pregnancies carried to term, as well as increased death rates from injury, suicide, and homicide. A study from New Zealand in 2006 showed higher rates of major depression, suicidal ideation, illicit drug dependence, and overall mental health problems.

One of the UK's two leading Christian groups involved in post-abortion counselling lists the following common complaints:

- Feeling the need to 'replace' the baby
- A feeling of distance from or, conversely, over-protectiveness of existing children
- Inability to maintain normal routine
- Depressed feelings stronger than 'a little sadness'
- Sleeping problems
- Flashbacks
- Tearfulness
- Relationship tensions or breakdown resulting from the abortion

Consent and the father

While the extent of some of these risks to the woman may still be uncertain, acknowledging that they definitely or possibly exist has significant implications for the question of informed consent. It is universally accepted within medical ethics that patients agreeing to any interventionist procedure must know enough about the possible side effects to be able to make their own balanced judgments as to whether they wish to proceed.

There has been very little research, so that little is known about the effect of abortion on fathers. Many men never learn from the woman in question that she has become pregnant, but where they have been informed, abortion diminishes the significance of fatherhood. Men have

LINKS *CMF File 35, 2007. www.cmf.org.uk/publications/content.asp?context=article&id=1985*

Consent for any surgical procedure normally includes a clear discussion of adverse consequences.

Is your patient really aware of the long term complications?

Psalm 139:13 For you created my inmost being; you knit me together in my mother's womb.

no legal rights to stop the abortion of their children. Experience suggests that only a quarter accompany their partners when they go to apply for a termination, and the other 75% are never sought by general practitioners or by the clinics. This significant interpersonal event thus becomes treated by all as if only one person, the woman, were involved.

Effect on the population

There is anecdotal evidence that, following an abortion, other children in the family may experience depression, obsessions about babies, or eating or sleep disorders. It has been suggested that a living child may identify with an aborted sibling. More research should be conducted in this area.

There are two ways in which the practice of abortion affects whole societies – quantitatively through the numbers of children actually born, and qualitatively through the effect abortion has on attitudes and other behaviour.

In England almost one pregnancy in four ends in abortion, and this contributes significantly to the fact that total fertility rates are now well below the rate needed for population replacement. In other words, not enough children are being born to replace the adults who die, and were it not for immigration, the total population number would be falling. At the same time, people are living longer so together with this increase in longevity, the decline in the birth rate (with consequent reduction in the numbers of those of working age) strains the funding of pensions and National Insurance, with consequent pressures on health and social services.

think it over...

1 How many women presenting for abortion are likely to be aware of these complications?

2 How can the risks be presented sensitively?

3 What alternatives to abortion can you think of? Would you know how to access them?

TAKE HOME MESSAGE: Proper counselling of patients requesting abortion requires acknowledgement of the potential complications *think....about the beginning of life...*

contraceptives

Many theologians have argued that the unitive and procreative aspects of sex need to be held together within a marriage relationship.
John Wyatt

Discussions on contraception often centre on when life begins. This subject is considered in more depth in Think 9, and clearly has implications for prescribing contraception. If a method of contraception acts after we consider life to begin, should we prescribe it?

Contraception is not just a question for GPs and gynaecologists. Surgeons need to consider thromboembolic risk in patients on the combined pill, and decreasing age at first intercourse means that paediatricians become involved. Probably only geriatricians are exempt! To consider contraception fully, let's look at some fundamental questions.

Should we use it at all?

Catholic churches do often question whether contraception should be used at all – but such discussion is today rare today in evangelical circles. Yet at the beginning of the last century, the Anglican Church also opposed 'artificial contraception', and a Google search soon proves that there are a number of evangelicals who still hold this position. Some arguments against contraception are based on a notion of what is 'natural' and what is not. Others use Bible verses, such as Genesis 1:28 where Adam and Eve are told to 'fill the earth and subdue it'. Was this just a direct command for Adam and Eve, or does the current global population suggests that the 'fill' part of this command has already been carried out? Few Christian GPs don't prescribe contraception at all, but more avoid certain methods.

Who is contraception for?

Many patients who ask for contraception are not married, and some Christians find these situations uneasy. There will be concerns about facilitating sin by giving something that might seem to encourage sexual activity outside marriage – but there

will also be worry that refusing to provide contraception will lead to an unwanted pregnancy, and a subsequent abortion request. Our approach to these situations will depend on our approach to Harm Reduction (Think 29).

Others will be under-16. Whilst the challenges regarding marriage are the same, additional questions over child protection and law arise here.

Some Christians do avoid prescribing for unmarried couples, which can be controversial. We may be seen to object to a particular patient, rather than a type of treatment, even if this isn't intended.

What should we prescribe?

For Christian doctors who believe life to begin at conception, there will be problems with some methods of contraception that may act after conception. Scientific evidence changes from time to time, as do the methods themselves, and research in this area is often limited.

To summarise simply, any barrier method, or sterilisation, obviously acts prior to fertilisation, so does not pose a problem. The combined pill, Cerazette, Depo-Provera and Implanon would all normally prevent fertilisation if used correctly, although the very occasional incidence of ovulation, with subsequent reliance on a post-fertilisation mechanism, cannot be ruled out.

More difficult are coils (Intra-uterine devices), progesterone-only pills other than Cerazette, and emergency contraception (the morning-after pill – considered in more detail in Think 8). Copper coils may sometimes act after fertilisation, although this appears less likely with progesterone releasing coils (like Mirena, commonly used for menorrhagia). However, rare cases of ectopic pregnancy with the Mirena in situ suggest that fertilisation can still occur. Progesterone-only pills may also act post-fertilisation, as they do not always prevent ovulation, and again, ectopic

Laurence Crutchlow wrote as a GP in London, based on a seminar given at National Student Conference 2011

Education of both men and women is a wonderful contraceptive.

The best contraceptive is the word no – repeated frequently.
Margaret Smith

pregnancies do occasionally occur. It is important to work out our position. A number of Christian GPs avoid prescribing the morning-after pill, progesterone-only pills, and fitting coils in the light of the above. Others will prescribe, but might not use such methods for themselves. Challenges might arise when a treatment like a Mirena coil is clearly indicated for menorrhagia (with contraception essentially a side-effect), but where it is unlikely that a patient will want to use alternative contraception.

More commonly, colleagues find this form of conscientious objection much more difficult to understand than with abortion – perhaps because of less discussions, and objection being less common.

Patients may also be surprised by any objection – particularly in a culture where doctors' autonomy is diminished. If you choose not to prescribe certain methods, you need to work out how you will approach this. You still need to inform patients that these methods exist, and need to think how you will pass them on to a colleague if you are not willing to prescribe yourself. This is particularly important with the morning-after pill, where delay makes the treatment less effective.

Ourselves

It is easy to see contraception as purely clinical. Yet many junior doctors will be married or considering marriage – but not yet feel ready or able to be parents. We may not necessarily choose ourselves to use everything we would prescribe to our patients. We need to consider the questions above not just for our patients, but also for ourselves, remembering that whatever contraception we use, God is ultimately sovereign over if and when children are born.

ed's thoughts...

Only two generations ago, doctors didn't have to grapple with 'what works when?' questions of contraception. Hormonal contraceptives didn't exist. Options have widened markedly, reflecting (or perhaps driving) changes in society, where contraception for unmarried and even underage women is seen as routine. With so much energy expended on working out what to do, much Christian discussion on contraception can easily miss the 'how' questions - how will we interact with patients who request contraception, and in what way can we show Jesus love to them as we see them?

think it over...

1 Should we use contraception at all?

2 How do we deal with unmarried patients who request contraception?

3 In the light of your view on when life begins, which methods do you think acceptable?

4 If you choose not to prescribe a particular contraceptive, how will you explain that to patients?

TAKE HOME MESSAGE: **We need to know both the ethics and the science to determine what to do**

43

Ethics of abortion

I t is striking how the age-old debate about abortion seems to have changed irreversibly just in the last few years. The stereotyped confrontation between the 'right to life' of the fetus and the 'right to choose' of the mother has become much more complex. Some commentators are now talking about the 'new ethics of abortion'. So what are the factors which have changed the debate so profoundly?

Firstly, there is much greater public awareness of the development of the unborn child, particularly because of widespread antenatal ultrasound screening and publicity for advances in fetal physiology.

Secondly, continuing advances in neonatal intensive care mean that survival of extremely preterm infants at 23 and 24 weeks is now almost routine. Many parents, families and professionals are exposed to the remarkable sight of tiny infants attached to all the paraphernalia of life support machinery. Charities and individuals donate many thousands of pounds to buy intensive care equipment for their local baby unit.

Thirdly, there has been remarkable growth in antenatal screening for fetal malformations and genetic abnormalities, and an increasing 'medicalisation' of pregnancy. The new consumerist rhetoric of 'providing choices for pregnant women' has become widespread. The growth of antenatal screening has 'medicalised' pregnancy by raising the expectation that medical expertise can provide a baby free from impairment or illness, and that it would be 'selfish' or even 'antisocial' for parents not to avail themselves of this service.

Fourthly, another major development is the growth of the disability rights movement. One eloquent voice is Tom Shakespeare, an academic sociologist who has achondroplasia. In the 1998 publication *Disability and Society*, he argues that 'disabled people are not consulted on matters which affect us:

John Wyatt wrote as Professor of Neonatal Paediatrics

professionals, un-representative charities and governments all make decisions about disability, without considering that the best experts on life as a disabled person are disabled people themselves. Politicians, scientists and doctors alike must realise that disabled people do have a particular interest in prenatal testing and should therefore be systematically involved in the public debate'. Many disabled people regard antenatal testing as a form of social discrimination against people like them.

In the new debate the social dimension is increasingly coming to the fore. The truth is that in many cases abortion represents an attempt to provide a quick technological fix – a medical, technical solution to what is a complex social phenomenon. But medicine alone cannot solve the age-old human dilemmas of the unwanted or disabled child. And women and health professionals contemplating abortion cannot regard this decision as a purely private, medical one. The social context of abortion and its implications for society as a whole cannot be ignored.

A Christian response

So how can Christian doctors and health professionals make a practical contribution to the debate? While we must seek to protect the vulnerable fetus from abuse, we must never forget the human pain at the heart of these complex issues. The truth is that many women (and their partners) are carrying painful and secret memories of past abortions. Instead of criticism and judgement, our duty is to empathise, to enter into the experience of pain, despair and perplexity.

Firstly, we must continually learn from the example of Christ. The Incarnation and the Cross are both supreme examples of empathy in action. Jesus did not condemn from the outside. He experienced humanity from the inside. He entered into human pain and perplexity, in order to transform

LINKS *Triple Helix*, Summer 2000. www.cmf.org.uk/literature/content.asp?context=article&id=886

Practical, supportive caring is never an easy alternative

Pregnancy: a symbol of hospitality

1 Peter 4:9 **Offer hospitality to one another without grumbling.**

TAKE HOME MESSAGE: **Abortion is much more complex than a simple 'it's wrong**

it with forgiveness and hope. So whenever we engage in the abortion debate we should do so with sensitivity, with gentleness and with compassion.

Secondly, as health care professionals, we must not limit our involvement to the biological and medical aspects of pregnancy. Elaine Storkey expresses sensitively the intuitive sense of wonder and the emotional demands of pregnancy from the mother's perspective.

'Pregnancy is itself a symbol of deep hospitality. It is the giving of one's body to the life of another. It is a sharing of all that we have, our cell structure, our blood stream, our food, our oxygen. It is saying 'welcome' with every breath, and every heartbeat... the growing fetus is made to know that here is love, here are warm lodgings, here is a place of safety.'

The concept of pregnancy as hospitality has deep resonances with Christian thinking about community and neighbourliness to strangers.

Thirdly, we should identify with those who feel stigmatised and rejected by the practice of antenatal screening and termination. However admirable and compassionate our motives, when we contemplate abortion for a malformed fetus we are sending an implicit message of rejection: we don't wish to accept this new other, to offer basic human hospitality.

Fourthly, we must concentrate on finding and developing practical, realistic alternatives. The way of practical, supportive caring is never an easy alternative. It is costly in terms of time, emotional involvement and financial commitment. But it is an essential response if Christians who defend the rights of the unborn are not to be guilty of hypocrisy.

The challenge is to find ways of translating Christian caring into clinical practice which are relevant and intelligible to modern

think it over...

1 If you don't refer for or perform abortions, how can you demonstrate care and compassion to a patient who will often be angry that you haven't referred them?

2 How would you counter someone who said that in times of shortage, it was appropriate to abort babies who would be disabled to save money?

3 Can you think of any new factors that have affected the abortion debate in the last 10 years? What might be a Christian response to these?

think.... about the beginning of life...

The morning after pill

Emergency contraception is not as reliable as planned, regular contraception

The morning after pill, one form of emergency contraception, was hailed as the government's answer to ever rising rates of teenage pregnancies and abortions. But research published in the *British Medical Journal* (*BMJ*) shows the failure of this policy. Figures for England and Wales now top the 200,000 per year mark, up 12% in ten years.

Sexual health expert Professor Anna Glasier, director of family planning at Lothian primary care NHS trust in Edinburgh, wrote in the *BMJ* 'Despite the clear increase in the use of emergency contraception, abortion rates have not fallen in the UK'. She summarised that the pill 'will prevent pregnancy in some women some of the time', but that, 'if you are looking for an intervention that will reduce abortion rates, emergency contraception may not be the solution'.

A cold reality

All this is sad news for the teenagers involved and we should not gloat over a massive public policy failure. No pill can protect against the emotional heartbreak of a broken relationship; and what can doctors say to a teenager made infertile by Chlamydia?

So what can we do? 'They'll do it anyway so we must limit the damage', is the sad refrain from most of the sexual health lobby. Many teenagers who do have sex wish they had waited and most want the age of consent raised and clearer boundaries from parents.

The Bible, with its wisdom on human nature, has some excellent advice on happy relationships and disease avoidance: 'The prostitute reduces you to a loaf of bread' (Proverbs 6:26) or, 'Fear the Lord and shun evil. This will bring health to your body' (Proverbs 3:7-8). But since most of today's movers and shakers, with their entrenched ideological stance on personal autonomy, dump anything biblical we must use the powerful evidence now available from clinical studies.

There is hope

Recently I asked a Ugandan doctor, Bernard Opar, how they reduced the HIV rate from 35% to 6% in his country. 'Firstly everyone said, "Abstinence till married" ', he replied. 'Later we added, "Be faithful to your spouse".' An important new study in the *American Journal of Obstetrics and Gynecology* confirms this abstinence only approach in delaying sexual activity. This was based on over 25,000 middle school students and demonstrated increased knowledge and a shift in attitude towards delaying sexual activity. Other studies highlight parental influence as one of the few factors known to influence teenage sexual behaviour. The presence of a father at home and having sex education from parents helps delay age of first intercourse.

No pill can protect against the emotional heartbreak of a broken relationship

So as doctors we must actively promote evidence based support for the family, for marriage and for sexual abstinence outside marriage. This is personally costly and, in the UK, will evoke surprise and at times strong and emotional opposition. But it's worth it when you see the light dawning on the face of a youngster who realises they need not have sex yet.

Mark Houghton wrote as a portfolio GP

Nucleus, 2006. www.cmf.org.uk/publications/content.asp?context=article&id=1878

testimony

Malcolm says ... I've tried several different approaches to the morning after pill. As a GP registrar I asked my trainer to prescribe it. After qualification in a smaller and more rural practice I sometimes did prescribe it. I was often in surgery on my own, so didn't have the opportunity to pass the request to another doctor, and it was not easy for patients to get it from anywhere else without delay - though I did always explain how it might work to the patients (and one or two chose not to use it with this knowledge).

Now I work in an urban Christian practice where we've all agreed not to prescribe. But many patients, aware of our approach, go elsewhere, so we lose any opportunity for discussion: I still don't feel I have a 'right' answer.

No pill can protect against emotional heartbreak

Ecclesiastes 11:5 As you do not know the path of the wind, or how the body is formed in a mother's womb, so you cannot understand the work of God, the Maker of all things

ed's thoughts...

There is a lot of controversy over whether the morning after pill can be deemed as contraception at all. For many who believe life begins at conception, there will be concerns over any 'contraceptive' that may prevent implantation rather than conception. Older morning after pill regimes fell into this category, but the limited literature available suggests that the currently favoured Levonelle regime usually (though not necessarily always) acts by delaying ovulation. The product literature for the new EllaOne pill suggests the same, although *The Lancet* notes that an effect on the endometrium (which might prevent implantation) cannot be ruled out, which the Faculty of Sexual and Reproductive Healthcare at the Royal College of Obstetricians and Gynaecologists acknowledges.

Ambiguity of science makes deciding whether to prescribe more difficult. Choosing not to can be costly. However, there is a wide variety of ways to obtain the morning after pill (such as pharmacies). Usually, a woman should be able to obtain it easily enough should a doctor choose not to prescribe – whether on conscience grounds, or simply because they believe the pill to be poor medicine given the statistics opposite. Christians have differed in their answer to this question – work out where you stand (and why), and then stand firmly. If you don't prescribe, work out what you will say to patients. If you do prescribe, consider how you might explain this to Christian doctors who don't agree.

think it over...

1 Do you prescribe the morning after pill? Give your reasons why or why not.

2 What might you do to reduce the need for emergency contraception in your patients?

3 What words might you use to introduce abstinence into a discussion about contraception?

TAKE HOME MESSAGE: The morning after pill does not appear to have reduced pregnancy or STI rates

THINK 09 *think… about the beginning of life…*

neonatal ethics

An extremely premature baby is born at 23 weeks of gestation, 17 weeks before term. The baby weighs just 500 grams. With full intensive care approximately 50% of these babies will survive, but many will have long-term developmental problems. Should intensive care be started or should the baby be allowed to die peacefully?

Thirty years ago less than 20% of babies born before 28 weeks of gestation survived. But over the last 30 years advances in medical care at the beginning of life have transformed the prospects of survival for babies born extremely prematurely. Currently in major centres in the UK more than 80% will survive, and many babies are now surviving at 23 weeks' gestation.

Up to 20% of extremely premature survivors will have an obvious disability such as cerebral palsy and many more will have evidence of educational or behavioural difficulties at school age. This begs the question, is attempting to save the life of these vulnerable babies a wise use of resources?

It is not only premature babies who raise ethical dilemmas. Some babies are born with serious complicated congenital malformations. Others have profound brain injury as a result of hypoxia at birth, or congenital infection. Should an attempt be made to treat such babies or would it be more ethical to withhold medical treatment?

A founding principle of neonatology is that every baby deserves the very best care, medical treatment and protection from harm. Behind this is the belief that every baby, however small or sick, has intrinsic value as a unique human person.

The Old Testament principle of defending the defenceless has been translated into a duty of care and respect for the weakest and most vulnerable members of our society.

John Wyatt wrote as Professor of Neonatal Paediatrics

If we are to take this Christian duty seriously we should be advocates on behalf of those who cannot speak up for themselves, and defend newborn babies and other vulnerable patient groups from those who might abuse or maltreat them.

Every baby, however small or sick, has intrinsic value as a unique human person

Most neonatal health professionals regard the deliberate killing of newborn babies as not only illegal but unethical, because it is incompatible with respect for the intrinsic value of human life. However, treating babies with respect and care does not mean that we are compelled to provide intensive treatment in every situation that arises. Despite spectacular advances in medical technology, there are some babies who cannot benefit from medical treatment and death is inevitable. In such cases it seems clear that withdrawing or withholding intensive care is an ethical and appropriate option.

The problem then is weighing up the burdens and benefits of intensive medical treatment. If there is no hope of long-term survival and intensive support is merely prolonging the process of dying, withdrawal of medical treatment, following full discussion and with the agreement of the parents, is most consistent with a genuine respect for the dignity of the individual.

When health professionals and parents recognise that intensive treatment should be withdrawn or withheld, it is important to realise that although medical treatment may stop, caring must never stop. We must provide the highest quality of terminal care for dying babies, just as we should provide terminal or palliative care for every dying adult.

LINKS *CMF File 27, 2004. www.cmf.org.uk/publications/content.asp?context=article&id=143*

testimony

09

Nathalie says... After being born at only 24 weeks' gestation, one baby was initially ventilated and progressed well, eventually just requiring low-flow oxygen. Sadly he was re-intubated after becoming septic a few weeks later. The procedure was complex, and his lungs became very stiff while we were having to bag ventilate him. At one point his heart rate fell to 18 bpm and his oxygen saturation to 24%. I started to wonder just what kind of damage this was doing to his brain and other organs. Were we doing the right thing and how many times were we going to try?

I wondered what God wanted – were we trying to play God in resuscitating the baby, or would stopping our attempts be worse? Jesus greatly valued small children and even said 'for the kingdom of heaven belongs to such as these'. He honoured our attempts and in the end he granted us success – after multiple septic episodes and re-intubations the baby survived and two months later was discharged. Who knows who that child will grow up to become?

Only at 24 weeks does a baby have legal rights

Matthew 19:14 **Jesus** said, 'Let the little children come to me, and do not hinder them, for the kingdom of **heaven** belongs to such as these.'

Each dying baby deserves tender loving care. Loving cuddles, where possible from mother, father or other close relative, are a physical demonstration of the tender care and respect that we owe to each baby. Many parents look back with sadness but also with fond memories to a special time they spent cuddling their dying baby. Caring for dying babies and their families is costly and difficult but it is an important and rewarding part of modern neonatal care.

The death of a newborn baby is one of the most devastating psychological traumas a parent can sustain, often with lifelong consequences. Siblings can also be profoundly affected by the death of a long-expected brother or sister. Health professionals need to ensure that emotional and practical support is provided for parents and for siblings, before, during and after the death. Many professionals too can suffer from the emotional costs of providing this level of care and it is important that support mechanisms are in place for them.

think it over...

1 What other patients might be vulnerable in the same way as a premature baby?

2 How would you respond to someone who argues that neonatal intensive care diverts resources from 'deserving' adult patients who are more likely to do well?

3 Some have suggested Christians should preserve life at all costs. Why might this not be right?

TAKE HOME MESSAGE: **Every baby, however ill, is formed in the image of God**

What is a Person?

The mass of the human body is made up of just six elements: oxygen, carbon, hydrogen, nitrogen, calcium, and phosphorus.

What does it mean to be a person? Is it possible to be a human being but not a person? What duties do we owe to persons as opposed to non-persons? Disagreements about personhood lie at the heart of many current bioethical debates, including those involving stem cell manipulations, prenatal screening, medical infanticide, the persistent vegetative state, dementia and psychiatric illness.

Modern approaches

For centuries it was generally accepted that the terms 'person' and 'living human being' were virtually equivalent. But over the last two decades, a number of influential modern philosophers, including Peter Singer and John Harris, have challenged traditional understandings of personhood. For Peter Singer a person is a being who has a capacity for enjoyable experiences, for interacting with others and for having preferences about continued life.

Once this kind of definition is accepted, there are a number of logical implications. Firstly, it is immediately obvious that in order to be regarded as a person, you must have an advanced level of brain function. In fact you must have a completely developed and normally functioning cerebral cortex. Secondly, there must be a significant group of human beings who are non-persons. These include fetuses, newborn babies and infants who lack self awareness, and a large group of children and adults with congenital brain abnormalities, severe brain injury, dementia and major psychiatric illnesses.

Thirdly, there are many non-human beings on the planet who meet the criteria of persons. These include at least chimpanzees, gorillas, monkeys and dolphins, but may also include dogs, pigs and many other mammals.

John Wyatt
wrote as Professor of
Neonatal Paediatrics

Singer argues that to make moral distinctions on the basis of species is to be guilty of a new crime, 'speciesism'. Instead we should make moral distinctions on the basis of 'ethically relevant characteristics', such as the ability to choose and value your own life.

Of course there are major logical problems with this kind of definition. In effect Singer has replaced one form of discrimination with another. Instead of discriminating on the basis of species, we should discriminate on the grounds of cortical function. In fact if we are into name-calling we could call him a 'corticalist'. But why should corticalism be preferable to speciesism?

A Christian perspective

At the heart of this secular philosophical perspective is the idea that you earn the right to be called a person by what you can do, by demonstrating that your brain is functioning adequately, by thinking and choosing. So how do we respond as Christians? What does it mean to be a person in the light of the Christian revelation?

Just as the three persons of the Trinity are individually unique, yet give themselves continually in love, so each human person is unique, yet made for relationship with others. Personhood is not something we can have in isolation – in Christian thinking it is a relational concept. Descartes came up with the famous statement, 'I think, therefore I am'. It's a definition that led ultimately to the modern concepts of Singer and Harris. By contrast we might suggest an alternative Christian version, 'You love me, therefore I am'. My being comes not from my rational abilities but from the fact that I am known and loved – first of all by God himself, and secondly by other human beings. This is why the experience of rejection and isolation can be so psychologically devastating, and why children

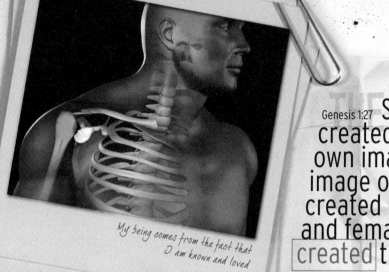

10

First, I'm trying to prove to myself that I'm a person.
Then maybe I'll convince myself that I'm an actress.
Marilyn Monroe

My being comes from the fact that
I am known and loved

Genesis 1:27 So God created man in his own image, in the image of God he created him; male and female he created them.

who have never experienced love and acceptance fail to develop into normal healthy adults. But even if I am rejected by other humans, I am still a person.

Doing or being?

For Peter Singer my personhood depends on what I can do, on the functioning of my cerebral cortex. But in Christian thinking my personhood rests on who I am, on the fact that God has called me into existence, and continues to know and love me.

This Christian understanding of personhood is much more permanent, more resilient, than the secular one. As we saw, to Peter Singer your personhood might disappear at any moment if your cortex started to malfunction. But in Christian thinking, whatever happens to you in the future, whatever disease or accident may befall your central nervous system, even if you are struck down by dementia or enter a persistent vegetative state, you will still be you: a unique and wonderful person known and loved by God. It is God's love that preserves our identity throughout the whole of our lifetime – whatever tragic and unexpected events may befall us – and on into eternity. And even when we were in our mother's womb, God was loving us and calling us into existence.

Conclusion

What does it mean to be a person? It's not just a question of academic philosophy. As Christian medics we are called to demonstrate the reality of what we believe. It is by our behaviour, by our compassionate caring, by our sensitivity and respect for the dignity of every patient, the helpless, the confused, the malformed, the unborn and the disabled, that we can really provide the answer.

think it over...

1 What implication does personhood have on medical care in
a) a patient with advanced dementia?
b) a baby born at 23 weeks' gestation?
c) a patient with severe mental illness?

2 If the fetus is a person, how does this affect our attitude to him or her?

3 All Christians should be guilty of 'speciesism'. Discuss.

TAKE HOME MESSAGE: **Personhood depends on who we are, not what we do**

51

Status of the embryo

For you created my inmost being;
you knit me together in my mother's womb.
— Psalm 139:13

The moral status of the human embryo is central to contemporary debates on the ethics of cloning, embryo research, stem cell research, genetic engineering, assisted reproduction, preimplantation diagnosis, genetic screening, post-coital contraception and the production of chimeras and animal-human hybrids. The issue is still vigorously debated in both medical and Christian literature. Christians have disagreed on the issue throughout history, and because of its practical implications for medical practice the debate amongst Christian doctors continues.

Biologically the human embryo is undoubtedly human; it has human chromosomes derived from human gametes. It is also undoubtedly alive – a new active individual human organism from the moment of fertilisation exhibiting respiration, growth, reproduction, excretion and nutrition. Human development is a continuous process beginning with fertilisation; essentially the only differences between zygote and full term baby being nutrition and time. Rather than speaking of it as 'a potential human being' it therefore makes more sense to speak of it as 'a human being with potential', 'a human being in an early stage of development' or 'a potential baby or adult'.

A philosophical defence of the human embryo is based on the principle that every human being has a right to life and human beings must not be discriminated against on the basis of age, sex, race, disability or any other biological characteristic. To argue that embryos can be killed in circumstances where older human beings cannot is therefore to employ a type of ageism.

A biblical defence of the human embryo is based on the idea that human beings are made in the image of God and belong to God and therefore should not be killed (Genesis 9:6).

Peter Saunders
wrote as CMF General Secretary

God's image is endowed by grace; conferred from outside, and therefore not contingent on any intrinsic properties: shedding of 'innocent' blood is uniformly condemned throughout Scripture.

Human beings include embryos as affirmed by many specific biblical references to life before birth. Psalm 139:13-16 affirms God's creation of, and communion with, the embryo-fetus in the womb as well as implying continuity between life before and after birth. God calls Isaiah and Jeremiah before birth and forms Job 'in the womb' as well as bringing him out of it. Most fundamentally, human nature is identical to the human nature of Christ who 'became flesh' at a moment of time (John 1:14 employs the aorist tense in Greek!), at conception, and who 'was made like us in every way' (Hebrews 2:17). In other words, if Christ's human life began as an embryo then so did ours.

devaluing any human life is inconsistent with God's justice

Christian ethical teaching is that we must love as Christ himself loved, that the strong should lay down their lives for the weak. To suggest the weak may be sacrificed in the interests of the strong is not biblical.

Some Christians employ 'secular' arguments to justify embryo experimentation or post-coital contraception, but other also use 'biblical' arguments. First, it is argued that the Bible itself teaches by implication that embryos are less valuable than children or adults on the basis of an interpretation of Exodus 21:22-25. In short, the verses have been misinterpreted in two ways. The Authorised Version and Revised Standard Version translations of the original Hebrew imply different punishments for the accidental killing of a mother (death penalty) and her unborn

11

*My frame was not hidden from you
when I was made in the secret place.*
Psalm 139:15

child (a fine). Some authors have concluded from this that God himself apportions different values to mother and fetus. The New International Version translation, by contrast, implies that the death penalty was for fetal or maternal death, and the fine was for injury without fetal or maternal death. This latter interpretation is now accepted as correct by most contemporary scholars.

Second, the view that the image of God was lost at the Fall was taken by Athanasius and accepted in part by Luther and Calvin. This has led some authors to suggest that human beings have lost the right to protection along with the image, although Luther and Calvin never suggested this and Scripture itself teaches that the death penalty for murder (killing an innocent human being) was instituted after the Fall and was based on the fact that man was made in God's image.

A third line of argument is to justify embryo disposal on the grounds that embryos don't have souls, but rather that the soul enters the body at a later point. This has been argued from Exodus 21 and also from Hebrews 10:5, which speaks prophetically of Christ in saying 'a body you prepared for me'. However the danger in generalising from the specific case of Christ is that whilst he was 'pre-existent', ordinary human beings are not. Regardless, the natural reading of the biblical account of Christ's incarnation is that this occurred at conception (Luke 1:29-36 or Matthew 1:20), and surely in the case of any doubt about when a new human being comes into existence, the benefit of that doubt should be given to the embryo. The idea that human beings can be divided into body and soul is based on the ancient Greek idea of body and soul being separate entities; a notion which finds no support in Scripture.

Every human being has potential

Matthew 1:20 Joseph son of David, do not be afraid to take Mary home as your wife, because what is conceived in her is from the Holy Spirit.

think it over...

1 Have you decided on the status of the embryo?

2 Are your views and practice about embryo research, the morning after pill and other related issues consistent with your view of the embryo?

3 How might you explain your position on the status of the embryo to:
a) a Christian colleague who disagrees with you
b) a senior colleague when refusing to take part in a certain treatment
c) a non-Christian patient who asks about your views?

think... about the end of life...

What does the Bible say about euthanasia?

Society always is attempting to make the physician into a killer... It is the duty of society to protect the physicians from such requests.
Margaret Mead

Is it ever right to perform euthanasia? We can't simply look up the word 'euthanasia' in a concordance – but there is much we can infer from Scripture by applying the principles that are there.

There are in fact two instances of voluntary euthanasia in the Bible.

In the first, Abimelech, believing himself to be fatally wounded, asks his armour-bearer to kill him. His request is granted and the Israelite leader is thus spared the 'indignity' of being killed by a woman. The death is seen as just retribution for Abimelech's own murder of his seventy brothers, and we are not told what happened, if anything, to the armour-bearer (Judges 9:52-55).

In the second, an Amalekite despatches the mortally injured Saul, still alive after a failed attempt at suicide. 'I happened to be on Mount Gilboa' the young man said 'and there was Saul, leaning on his spear, with the chariots and riders almost upon him. When he turned around and saw me, he called out to me and I said, "What can I do?"...Then he said to me "Stand over me and kill me. I am in the throes of death but I am still alive." So I stood over him and killed him because I knew that after he had fallen he could not survive' (2 Samuel 1:6-9).

Whether the story (which varies from the account of Saul's death at the end of 1 Samuel 31) is true, or the Amalekite's fabrication in order to win favour in David's eyes for despatching Saul and delivering him the crown, the new king's reaction is interesting. 'Why were you not afraid to lift your hand to destroy the Lord's anointed?' (2 Samuel 1:14) he asks, and then apparently before receiving a reply, as if the confession in itself were sufficient grounds for a verdict to be made, orders the Amalekite's execution.

In the mind of David at least, the compassionate killing of Saul constituted a capital offence, despite him being in great pain (presumably with peritonitis) and close to death without the possibility of analgesia, and most significantly of all, despite Saul's own request to be killed.

The creation narrative tells us that human beings are unique in being made in the image of God and it is on this basis, after the flood, that God introduces to all humankind the death penalty for murder (Genesis 9:6). Human, being made in the image of God, are not to be unjustly killed.

This is later formalised in God's covenant agreement with his chosen people Israel in the sixth of the ten commandments, 'You shall not murder' (Exodus 20:13, Deuteronomy 5:17). But what does this mean? The English language has created for us a confusion that is not present in the original text. There are in fact ten Hebrew words translated 'kill' in the Authorised Version of the Bible, all with different shades of meaning, but only one of them is implicated in the sixth commandment, the word *ratsach*. Its Greek equivalent is *phoneuo* and its most accurate translation is 'murder' (NIV).

Other scriptural passages resolve any ambiguity for us and leave us with a precise definition of what is prohibited, namely the 'intentional killing of an innocent human being' (eg Numbers 35:20-21).

Euthanasia clearly falls within this biblical definition. There is no provision for killing on grounds of diminished responsibility (on the basis of age or illness) and there is no provision for compassionate killing, even at the person's request. Similarly there is no recognition of a 'right to die' as human life belongs to God and is not any human being's personal possession. Suicide is equally a breach of the sixth commandment. Only God has the authority to take human life. Human beings may only do so under God's delegated authority.

Loving God means obeying him and if God commands something clearly then that should be the end of any debate. However, many

Peter Saunders
wrote as CMF General Secretary

No man has power over the wind to contain it; so no one has power over the day of his death.
Ecclesiastes 8:8

Revelation 21:4 **He will wipe every tear from their eyes. There will be no more death or mourning or crying or pain, for the old order of things has passed away.**

Human life belongs to God

Christians today are not convinced that euthanasia is wrong in all circumstances.

With the patient dying in pain it may seem that we have only two equally undesirable alternatives to choose from – either 'living hell' or the euthanasia needle. In reality there is a third way – the way of the Cross. It calls us to expend our time, money and energy in finding compassionate solutions to bad situations and has found practical shape in the hospice movement and good palliative care – pioneered in large part by Christian doctors.

But perhaps the most powerful Christian argument against euthanasia is that death is not the end. God created a perfect world that has 'fallen' as a consequence of our rebellion as human beings against God. But God's intervention through Christ's death and resurrection on our behalf means that through faith we can look forward to a new world after death with God where there is 'no more death or mourning or crying or pain'. For those, however, who do not know God, euthanasia is not a 'merciful release' at all. It may rather be propelling them towards a judgment for which they are unprepared followed by eternal separation from God in Hell – thus it may be the worst thing we could ever do for them!

Euthanasia is wrong fundamentally because God has said it is wrong – and when, as Christians, we are tempted to consider it our response needs to be quite simply 'it is written; you shall not murder'. However, as well as being right, God's laws also make good sense. We can therefore argue effectively against the legalisation of euthanasia in a secular forum on grounds of protecting vulnerable people from abuse even when our opponents don't accept that God exists.

think it over...

1. Have you ever received a request for euthanasia from a patient? How did it make you feel?

2. What might you say if you were to receive such a request in future?

3. How would you explain that euthanasia is wrong to a Christian colleague who thought it the 'compassionate thing to do'?

TAKE HOME MESSAGE: **Euthanasia is fundamentally wrong**

12

55

think... about the end of life...

Why not legalise euthanasia?

Society's prohibition of intentional killing ... is the cornerstone of law and social relationships. It protects each of us impartially, embodying the belief that all are equal.
Luke Gormally

J **had been action man personified in work and sport, but several years of progressive multiple sclerosis with no remissions had left him almost tetraplegic.** *He was well looked after, with maximum nursing and homecare input. I visited regularly for support.*

After a couple of years, J suddenly asked, 'Doc, go out to your car, get something, and put me out of this. If I was an animal, you'd have to.' For a moment, my heart agreed with him, but then a lot of other realisations kicked in. 'J', I said, and I was so glad to be able to say this, 'that's against the law and I'm not going to do it. And you know I'm a Christian and what you've just said gives me a particular problem. But I'm glad you've raised it, because I hadn't realised how bad things had got, and I promise that from now on we're going to work twice as hard for you.'

J made the same request monthly for about two years. You will conclude I never performed euthanasia, although the story didn't end there.

All medics need to know the arguments for and against legalising euthanasia. There are three arguments **for**:

- We want it – the autonomy argument
- We need it – the compassion argument
- We can control it – the public policy argument

The Christian case **against** euthanasia can be stated very briefly. No Scripture can be found in favour and the sixth Commandment, 'You shall not murder', which prohibits the intentional killing of the legally innocent applies.

But as J's story illustrates, most of us will meet situations where we ask ourselves, however momentarily, 'Why does God say that?'

Andrew Fergusson wrote as CMF strategy adviser on euthanasia and former GP

Some objections to the arguments for euthanasia

We want it – the autonomy argument

Following the patient's autonomy impacts the doctor's. Where a patient's autonomy is followed so far that they receive a prescription for lethal medication or are put to death at the end of a needle, the doctor's autonomy is compromised.

Most patients have 'another question'

Those who care for the dying know the (relatively few) who currently ask for euthanasia usually have another question behind their question. This may be physical, psychosocial or spiritual – 'Why me?' or 'Why now?'

But there are deliberated requests! Why can't they have euthanasia?

J's requests were considered. Why with controls can't there be a law to accommodate exceptional cases? Bearing in mind inevitable uncertainty about prognosis, to change the law to allow euthanasia for this small minority within a minority would mean it was performed far more often when it was 'wrong' than when some would see it as 'right'.

Allowing 'voluntary' euthanasia won't end there

'Slippery slopes' exist. If we change the law to allow voluntary euthanasia for those who are suffering and have the capacity to ask for it, surely compassion means we should similarly provide euthanasia for that patient who is suffering at least as much but has no capacity to request it?

We need it – the compassion argument

Do we have to kill the patient to kill the symptoms? Palliative care has answered that question with a resounding 'No', though the harder symptoms to deal with are not positive physical ones but negative ones of patients' losses – the things they can't do any more. The challenge to healthcare becomes bringing meaning and hope in the face of suffering.

Nucleus, April 2005. www.cmf.org.uk/publications/content.asp?context=article&id=1586

testimony

Abi says... As a house officer, I once admitted a patient who had serious gangrene, and who was generally neglected. He was very low in mood and blamed himself for allowing his foot to become so bad. As I was clerking him, he asked whether I could give him some medicine to help him die as he felt he had no hope of recovery. I gently explained to him that this was not something that doctors were allowed to do, and reassured him that everything possible would be done to help him medically. I explained everything we were doing as we cared for him and provided constant reassurance. This helped ease his initial reluctance to be treated and he allowed us to continue. I offered him the option of psychiatric input the next day and ensured his mental health concerns were clearly documented along with his physical condition.

I found it important to be clear that I could not help this patient with his wish to die. It is also necessary to ensure that such patients receive support and compassion and that everyone involved in their care is aware of their situation. Praying for these patients when treating them or afterwards can also provide strength for you and the patient even if they are not aware of it!

We can control it – the public policy argument
As Dutch statistics confirm, we cannot control it. How ever could we, when the key witness, the person police would most want to interview, is dead?

Conclusion
All three arguments are tried and found wanting. Let us instead commit ourselves to working for that genuinely 'gentle and easy death' all our patients deserve. J eventually stopped asking for euthanasia. With no input from me, except prayer, he came to a quiet Christian faith. He died peacefully about five years later, 20 minutes after receiving communion.

Whose autonomy?

THE WORD

Psalm 119:50 My comfort in my suffering is this: Your promise preserves my life.

think it over...

1 How might you help patients to express the 'other questions' referred to before they lead to a euthanasia request?

2 Do you feel you have sufficient expertise in palliative care to work towards a 'gentle and easy death' when necessary? What steps could you take to learn more?

TAKE HOME MESSAGE: **Secular arguments for euthanasia do not stand up**

Advance directives

Afraid of being trapped between life and death, people have sought ways of telling doctors that if they can no longer express their wishes, they would rather be allowed to die than be kept alive by extraordinary or disproportionate means. Some have chosen to record this decision in a written document termed an advance directive, or 'living will'. Advance directives have appeared because of three key issues and influences within society.

Autonomy – the previous paternalistic mentality of 'the doctor knows best', has been replaced with the notion of 'informed consent' – the idea that clinicians give information so that patients can make sound choices.

Many institutions and professions are under suspicion. This loss of trust is not one-sided. Doctors are increasingly fearful that they will be sued if their patients don't like the outcome of any intervention; they are losing trust in their patients.

Both of these are set against ever-increasing medical capability. Seldom a week goes by without some new treatment being announced. However, while these advances often sustain life, many people find that they are left with a quality of life they feel unable to bear.

People argue that advance directives can help them to:

- avoid degrading and drawn-out treatment for a terminal illness
- achieve a death with dignity, or a 'good death'
- avoid medical costs during a prolonged final illness
  - avoid breaching a patient's personal or religious beliefs

A number of reasons why the situation is not straightforward:

Uncertain outcome – advance directives often state that 'in the event of 'x' medical condition occurring with no chance of recovery, I would want 'y' to be done'. In order for a doctor to carry out this directive he has to be certain of several things. First that he is certain in his diagnosis that the patient has 'x'. Secondly that there is no chance of recovery if given suitable treatment. This is seldom easy to do and people are known to make remarkable and unexpected recoveries.

New attitudes – trying to imagine what it would be like to be terminally ill is one thing. Being terminally ill is quite another. Many events in life can influence one's attitude to disability. The arrival of a grandchild can give an elderly person a new reason for wanting to continue living, and changes in religious conviction can revolutionise a person's attitudes to life, death and disability.

New treatments – when writing an advance directive, a person will make assumptions based on current abilities of technology to control pain or other symptoms. Developments in medical practice are increasing our ability to make life comfortable, and the advance directive may not be able to take these changes into account.

Finance and fraud – there is concern that people will be coerced into signing a directive, and that unscrupulous carers or potential beneficiaries may exploit the feeling of 'I don't want to be a burden to my carers'.

Any assessment of advance directives from a Christian viewpoint will start by acknowledging that each human being is made 'in the image of God', and as such every person has built-in value. This is regardless of any physical or intellectual capacity or any other characteristic. Christians need to resist any measures that may devalue human life, especially that of the most vulnerable people in society for whom God has special respect. Decisions about treatments should focus on a consideration of the benefits and burdens of any medical intervention, rather than viewing some states of existence as being excessively burdensome in themselves.

It would be better if advance directives were superfluous and people

Jim Paul wrote as a palliative care doctor. He is now a worker at L'Abri

testimony

Lotte says... An unconscious elderly man arrived in the Emergency Department by ambulance following an apparent overdose. His wife accompanied him, carrying a hand-written Advance Directive. But there was no record of a Directive held by the department, nor by the locum GP who had attended the patient at home and called 999. The directive, and the patient's wife, were clear that no treatment should be given other than palliation. Was the Directive valid? Was it really signed by the patient when competent to do so? On balance of probabilities? Yes, it probably did express his wishes. But was there any chance this was invalid? Any chance of malicious fraud or worse? Any chance that the patient may have changed his mind after signing it? Was there reasonable doubt? Yes. The default position of an Emergency Department is to save life. Reasonable discussion about withdrawing or withholding treatment comes later. On this occasion no treatment was necessary other than supportive care anyway. But a seed of doubt had been sown; staff were anxious that immediate action to save life might later be considered illegal. It is a very foolish and dangerous thing for priority to be given to a piece of paper rather than to a dying person.

Which priority: a piece of paper or a person?

trusted doctors to act wisely and humanely: fighting for life when there was a chance of success, and using palliative care when cure was no longer possible. Christian doctors should take a lead in working to establish a relationship of trust that uses their medical expertise, while recognising the personal expertise represented by each patient.

ed's thoughts...

Since writing, terminology has changed, and 'advance refusals' is a more common term than 'advance directives'. As 'advance refusal' has a legal definition that may not have been envisaged when the original was written, the wording has not been changed.

Ecclesiastes 3:1-2 There is a time for everything, and a season for every activity under heaven: a time to be born and a time to die, a time to plant and a time to uproot.

think it over...

1 When did a patient last express plans for the future to you? Might these affect their future treatment?

2 What could you do to help patients to trust you, so that directives might not be needed?

3 Why do you think many people are so worried about becoming dependent on others?

4 Might there be circumstances under which a Christian would have an advance directive?

TAKE HOME MESSAGE: **Advance directives have risks, and may not seem as simple as they appear**

I still miss those I loved who are no longer with me but I find I am grateful for having loved them. The gratitude has finally conquered the loss.
Rita Mae Brown

Christians in palliative care

Palliative care is 'the active total care of those who have advanced, incurable life-limiting illness'. Active care emphasises that there is much that can be done to control symptoms and maximise quality of life for patients who may otherwise feel that there is nothing more that can be done. It is also 'total' care in that it embraces a holistic approach to the care of both patients and their families, recognising that physical symptoms are only part of the needs of patients with advanced disease who are facing the prospect of dying. It thus integrates physical, emotional, spiritual and social aspects of care, and this of necessity requires a multidisciplinary team approach.

How I became involved

My first contact with palliative care was on my elective in a hospice. I found the experience extremely moving, and it proved to be a turning point in my career. This was holistic care as I had never encountered it before. I worked under a Christian consultant who was highly eminent and experienced, yet whose self-effacing humility, approachability and bedside manner were inspirational.

Christians need to be involved

Christians in every generation have been inspired to work with the destitute and dying. Dame Cicely Saunders is widely regarded as the founder of the modern hospice movement, with the establishment of St Christopher's Hospice in London in 1967. Both she and many of those who pioneered the subsequent expansion of hospice services were committed Christians, setting up facilities with the implicit aims of welcoming all and expressing the love of God in every aspect of patient care.

Jeff Stephenson wrote as a consultant in palliative medicine

UK palliative care services are generally well developed, and there is a wide range of services. As a result, we are well placed to influence attitudes to the care of the dying in other parts of the world; there are challenging opportunities for medical mission. It also gives us an important voice in the ever-present euthanasia debate.

Hospices are open to people of all faiths and none, but the term 'spiritual care' in the context of the hospice movement was originally defined in terms of our relationship to the Creator God. As it has expanded and moved back into mainstream healthcare, palliative care has become secularised and the dominant ethos is now humanism. The concept of spirituality has been broadened and watered down so that it is now very hard to define, and so spiritual care is difficult to provide.

Christians in every generation have worked with the dying

It is essential for more Christians to get involved in this work and to reclaim the ground. We are uniquely equipped to speak truth into the issues surrounding end of life care. We are called to follow Jesus into the dark places of suffering and minister where others fear to go. We have the ultimate hope in Christ: the truth that there is a God who loves us, who will come alongside us and enter into our suffering, who ultimately has conquered death and who offers eternal life to those who put their trust in him. While the deathbed is not the place for aggressive evangelism, opportunities to share the gospel do arise when situations are approached sensitively and with the Holy Spirit's leading. We can also minister in many ways without explicitly sharing our faith, and thereby demonstrate the love of Jesus.

Nucleus, July 2004. www.cmf.org.uk/literature/content.asp?context=article&id=726

testimony

I ain recalls... My first experience of palliative care was an 80 year old lady with severe heart failure who was increasingly short of breath leading to recurrent admissions to CCU. She was concerned about her breathlessness and immobility at home, and she worried about her husband's ability to cope.

We referred her to the palliative care team and she was started on Oramorph to relieve her breathlessness. The social worker and occupational therapists assessed her home needs. The aim was also to break the cycle of recurrent admissions with repeated unnecessary investigations, so that she could be managed at home in a more appropriate way. On discharge she was a bit less anxious about her husband as the community palliative care nurses were visiting regularly and home adaptations had been provided.

On reflection, we really didn't enquire about her spiritual needs. As a Christian, particularly with palliative care patients, it's so important to gently raise faith issues. Still, I admit that, unless an obvious opportunity presents itself, I still find it a difficult subject to raise.

Everyone needs compassion

How to get involved

This kind of work is not something that everyone can do. I encourage anyone thinking of becoming involved to meditate on John 11:20-38. In this passage we see Jesus' compassion and presence with Mary and Martha in their pain and his attitude to death. If you do feel that God is calling you into this work, try to spend some time in palliative care or a hospice. Many medical schools now include palliative care in the curriculum, but if yours does not then try to get some exposure in an elective, on a special study module or as a junior doctor. People die only once, and as carers we only get one chance to get it right. Christians have a huge amount to contribute.

John 11:33 **When Jesus saw her weeping...he was deeply moved**

TAKE HOME MESSAGE: **It is essential for more Christians to get involved in palliative care**

think it over...

1 What is my attitude to patients who cannot be cured?

2 Do I demonstrate Christ-like compassion to dying patients and their relatives?

3 Do I consider spiritual issues when caring for patients?

4 How can I learn to care more effectively for the terminally ill?

5 Is God calling me to a career in specialist palliative care?

Good physicians will know the limit of their art
G. Meilaender

Withholding and withdrawing treatment

When people are ill they tend to go to a doctor, nurse or another healthcare professional to ask for treatment. Diagnosing the cause of the person's illness and then working out what would be the best approach is a complex process and can easily be misunderstood by the patient.

Treatment may have to start before a diagnosis has been made. However, this carries the risk that the treatment may itself mask the true nature of the disease. A good doctor should always be considering whether the initial diagnosis was correct and be prepared to change his or her opinion if doubt starts to arise.

Sometimes patients mistake this change of opinion as the doctor making a mistake. However, the art of medicine involves making decisions on limited amounts of information and expecting to adjust or correct them as new evidence emerges.

Clinical decisions

Technology has developed to the point where it can be used to sustain the physical life of a body seemingly indefinitely. We can also treat conditions that if left alone would do little damage to the person. The majority of men are found to have enlarged or cancerous prostate glands at autopsy. However, these diseased organs did not cause them to die.

The discussion of withdrawing or withholding treatment is often seen as an ethical discussion. However, in all but the most extreme cases, it is more appropriate to see it as a matter of good clinical judgment. Treatments often carry risks, and a doctor needs to weigh up the balance between the potential for doing good and the potential for harm. People who are refused antibiotics when they have a sore throat often feel let down, but the doctor has been weighing up the small chance of the drugs making any difference, against the very real risk that over-use of antibiotics can lead to resistant bacteria developing.

It is more often an issue of good clinical judgement than an ethical dilemma

Respecting people

Christians base treatment decisions on the fundamental principle of respect for the sanctity of human life. This is not altered if a person is very old or very young, is physically able or has severe disabilities.

Where possible, people also have a right to make decisions about their own treatment. This includes the right to refuse any treatment even if that decision seems irrational.

Respecting people also means recognising their mortality. Over-treating patients fails to respect that a part of being human is to be mortal. It has also led to increasing demands for euthanasia, as people become frightened that they may be supported by medical technology beyond their ability to cope.

Best interest

One common guide is to look for the patient's 'best interest'. This can help when treating young children, or adults who are not fully conscious. In the past, best interest was almost always seen as prolonging life. However, a more complex assessment is needed now that medical technology can keep a person's body alive, perhaps inappropriately. Most people accept that there is no absolute duty to prolong life at all costs.

Duncan Vere
wrote as Emeritus
Professor of Therapeutics

LINKS   CMF File 7, 1999. www.cmf.org.uk/literature/content.asp?context=article&id=166

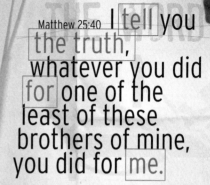

16

Respecting people means recognising their mortality

Matthew 25:40 **I tell you the truth, whatever you did for one of the least of these brothers of mine, you did for me.**

testimony

Matt says... What should you do for a 34 year old mother with cervical cancer and an infection, whom you suspect is dying? Treat with antibiotics or withhold them? What do you do once you have started? When is it time to withdraw?

Cases like this one in the hospice frequently raised tough questions for me. I know life is God-given, and I have been trained to save it – but at what cost? How far should we go with our treatments? Who, when all is said and done, are we treating; our patients or ourselves? How can you make decisions like these comfortably?

I have learnt that they can never be comfortable. Death is a sad reality of a fallen world, and we react with Jesus, weeping at Lazarus' tomb. Withdrawing treatment can feel like surrender to defeat – but I have begun to recognise that sometimes the most helpful and loving thing we can do is allow our patient to die.

TAKE HOME MESSAGE: **We must judge the worth of the treatment, not the worth of the patient**

think it over...

1 Can you think of circumstances when it is not appropriate to start treatment?

2 Can you think of times when you've seen too much (or too little) treatment given?

3 How does this apply to resuscitation as a treatment? Is it sometimes appropriate not to resuscitate someone?

4 Are you familiar with the Mental Capacity Act (2005), and how it might affect your approach in a patient unable to decide for themselves?

Brain death

Organ transplantation has developed from a highly innovative procedure to routine clinical practice. Successful kidney transplantation started in the 1950s followed by heart, liver and pancreas transplants in the 1960s, and lung and small bowel transplants in the 1980s. Outcomes have steadily improved due to better surgical techniques and more effective immunosuppressive treatments. One-year graft survival is currently 94% for live donor kidneys, 88% for deceased donor kidneys, 86% for livers, 84% for hearts and 77% for lungs. Longer term outcomes are similarly improving.

However, demand far exceeds the organs available. In the UK in the financial year 2007-8 there were 2,385 organs transplanted from 809 deceased donors with a further 839 live donor transplants, but there were 7,655 patients on the active waiting list. This list grows at 8% per year, but 1,000 die each year while waiting or become too ill for a transplant. While this shortfall persists, options will be considered to increase the number of available organs.

A key ethical issue is diagnosis of death. There is currently no legal definition of death, although 'an irreversible loss of the capacity for consciousness combined with irreversible loss of the capacity to breathe spontaneously and hence to maintain a spontaneous heartbeat' is generally accepted. A patient who has had no heart beat or spontaneous respiration for 24 hours, for example, is clearly dead to all concerned, yet tissues such as skin and cornea can still be taken and used.

A patient with irreversible damage to the brain stem, where the nerve centres controlling breathing and heartbeat are situated, will rapidly develop respiratory and circulatory arrest, although both functions can be artificially maintained on a ventilator for a variable period of days. It was for such patients on intensive care units that the criteria to diagnose brain stem death were developed. These criteria are needed irrespective of whether organ donation is being considered: it is always important to separate the treatment of the 'patient' from the treatment of the potential 'donor'.

There are two types of deceased donors: the heart-beating or donation-after-brain-stem-death (DBD) donor and the non-heart-beating or donation-after-cardiac-death (DCD) donor. The DBD donor will typically be on a critical care unit with severe brain injury and, when a clinical diagnosis of brain stem death is confirmed and providing consent is obtained, organs for transplantation may be removed.

There are different categories of DCD donors, but essentially a diagnosis of cardiac death will be made with cessation of heart beat and respiration, after treatment has been withdrawn because it is now medically futile. If consent has previously been obtained, and after a stand-off period to ensure there is no spontaneous return of cardiac function, then organs may be removed.

Brain stem death

Many philosophers, ethicists, theologians and clinicians have debated when is the exact point of death? There is no agreed view. What has been accepted is that death is a process. Likewise it is accepted that irreversible destruction of the brain stem has a dire prognosis with no prospect of recovery. Therefore the majority view is that brain stem death can be considered as the patient being dead, even while respiratory and circulatory functions are artificially maintained by a ventilator. This position is supported within law and by the Code of Practice for the diagnosis of brain stem death, which is currently being revised.

However, there is an opposing minority view that brain stem death

Keith Rigg wrote as a consultant transplant surgeon

LINKS   CMF File.36, 2008. www.cmf.org.uk/publications/content.asp?context=article&id=2079

17

Death, that hath suck'd the honey of thy breath,
Hath had no power yet upon thy beauty.
William Shakespeare

There is no legal definition of death

2 Corinthians 5:1 **Now we know that if the earthly tent we live in is destroyed, we have a building from God, an eternal house in heaven, not built by human hands.**

doesn't equate with death, until the heart has stopped beating and respiration has ceased. It is therefore only after the removal of organs that the patient can be considered truly dead. The criteria for brain stem death are therefore prognostic rather than diagnostic, and cessation of brain stem function is part of the process of dying rather than the point of death. The 1980 BBC *Panorama* – 'Transplants: are the donors really dead?' – espoused this view, but it has been repeated regularly over the years. It is likely there will always be opposing views, but what is important is that the public have confidence in the professionals and are helped to understand what is meant by brain stem death.

Cardiac death

Within the last decade there has been an increase in the number of DCD donors as a result of the decrease in DBD donors. The procedure is outlined above and although the majority have no ethical or legal concerns, there is an opposing view. The main issue relates to the stand-off period between the time of the heart stopping and perfusion of the organs prior to removal. For most tissues any period greater than 10 minutes is likely to mean injury caused by the circulation ceasing that will be detrimental to usage; while shorter periods may cause concerns about the certainty of death. Spontaneous auto-resuscitation or the 'Lazarus' phenomenon is rare, but may occur up to 10 minutes after the heart stops. Around the world stand-off times of 2, 5 or 10 minutes are used. In the UK 10 minutes is standard practice, although there are some intensive care specialists who feel this is not long enough. One recommendation of the Organ Donation Taskforce is to resolve outstanding legal, ethical and professional issues and this area requires clarification.

think it over...

1 Do Christians need to be concerned about brain stem death as a concept?

2 Is the risk of declaring someone dead too soon outweighed by the benefits of organ donation?

3 What do you think of an 'opt-out' system for organ donation? Does it raise concerns for a Christian?

TAKE HOME MESSAGE: **Defining death is not as easy as it appears**

Alternative medicine

There is no medicine like hope, no incentive so great, and no tonic so powerful as expectation of something better tomorrow.
Orison Swett Marden

Any list of alternative therapies will pull together an amazing diversity – from acupuncture and aromatherapy to reflexology and yoga. All have their own ideas about how to diagnose illness and maintain health, but the idea of life force or vital energy is common to many therapies.

This is claimed to be a non-physical energy that passes through the body. When flowing freely it enables health, but blockage or imbalance leads to disease. Treatment aims to manipulate that energy by different means. In acupuncture, with needles; in aromatherapy, with aromatic oils and in reflexology, through foot massage.

Why might it seem to work?
Of course some alternative treatments may genuinely work – for example herbal compounds from which modern medicines were derived. The placebo effect is present in all medicine, whether conventional or alternative, and can be increased by a number of factors, such as a patient having confidence in the therapist, or sharing their worldview.

Many patients use alternative therapies alongside conventional medicine. If they improve, who is to say where the effect came from? If they trust their homeopath more than their doctor, they may naturally attribute the improvement to the alternative. It may simply be that the illness has run its course, quite apart from the therapy used.

Many alternative therapies and practitioners place a commendable emphasis on good diet, regular exercise, rest and relaxation, stopping smoking and drinking less alcohol or coffee. These lifestyle modifications alone will produce major benefit for many conditions.

We must also accept that some healing may be demonic in nature. There is nothing to suggest that Satan cannot produce healing in order to deceive. Deuteronomy 13 makes it clear that not all miracles are from God.

Assessing a specific therapy
1. Do the claims fit the facts? – We should look for good trial data and be wary of small trials with subjective outcome measures or a lack of placebo control. This invalidates the majority of studies done on most alternative therapies. A journal called *Focus on Alternative and Complementary Therapy* regularly publishes good quality trial data – many of which fail to show conclusive evidence for the therapies tested.

2. Is there a rational scientific basis? – The theory underlying most orthodox medicine is soundly based on careful observation and evidence. There are still mysteries – we don't know how general anaesthetics really work, but there's no doubt they do, and a number of reasonable theories explain their action. Yet many alternative therapies are based on theories that run counter to the evidence, or have a very tenuous link with it.

3. What's the underlying worldview? – This is a crucial point. Many therapies are based on eastern religions that run completely counter to Christianity. Others may have more western origins but the worldview of the founders may concern us. We should be very wary of any talk of energy medicine or a therapy that seems to have mysterious actions that cannot be explained rationally, even more so if practitioners openly claim to use supernatural means for diagnosis or treatment. In some cases it may be possible to separate the theory from the practice itself, such as acupuncture. In others, such as Reiki, it is not.

Mark Pickering wrote as CMF Student Secretary

LINKS *Nucleus, January 2006. www.cmf.org.uk/publications/content.asp?context=article&id=1729*

testimony

Richard says... 'I like to use things that are natural, doctor', many patients tell me. But what is 'natural'? Most patients respond with horror if reminded that drugs like morphine or atropine are essentially 'natural'. Working in a fairly affluent part of London, I'm often asked about alternative treatments. Most patients assume all doctors will be against it, so are not surprised if I am sceptical. Indeed, I wonder how many use it but never tell me, fearing my reaction?

Conflicts come with treatments which sit uneasily on the borderline between conventional and alternative: Glucosamine for joint pain is a common example. Acupuncture is another. Prescribing and referral guidelines often tie my hands whatever my own views.

For me a bigger question arises. Many patients, when pushed, admit that alternative therapies have no good reason to work. Yet they still see those who use them. Why should this be? What element of care is missing from my own practice? How do I need to change?

Golden Mirror of Medicine from Qing Dynasty

1 Thessalonians 5:21 **Test everything. Hold on to the good.**

4. Is it medically safe? – Thankfully most alternative therapies have few potential side-effects. This could be simply because they have few specific effects beyond the placebo response. Perhaps the greatest danger is from a false sense of security, so that serious organic pathology, may be ignored while a patient neglects to see their doctor in favour of balancing up their energy levels with a friendly alternative practitioner.

Conclusion

As Christians our alternative is a middle ground, an alternative to two unhelpful extremes: conventional, evidence-based medicine with its tendency to focus on the pathology and forget the person. Alternative medicine's commendable focus on the individual and preserving balance, but a willingness to suspend critical thinking. Between the two should stand Christians, with a commitment to evidence-based practice, but also to care for the individual by communicating truth and showing genuine concern.

think it over...

1 What alternative treatments do you commonly come across?

2 Why should Christians be concerned about the idea of 'life-force'?

3 Might we have something to learn from alternative practitioners? If so, what?

TAKE HOME MESSAGE: **Not everything about alternative medicine is bad, but there are many dangers**

think....about....

CAM: acupuncture

The underlying concept is that of qi, or chi, an invisible life energy force which is thought to travel through the body along defined pathways called meridians
Dr Robina Coker

Acupuncture is a traditional form of Chinese medicine which involves stimulating the skin at strategic places, called acupuncture points, to produce therapeutic benefits. Usually this stimulation is done using fine needles.

Why might it work?

The first explanation for acupuncture came out of Chinese culture and belief. They held (and many still do) that there are two opposing life forces (Yin and Yang) which circulate in special channels (meridians) throughout the body. Disease is caused by an imbalance of these forces and can be rectified by regulating the flow of energy in these meridians. This can be achieved by stimulating acupuncture points located along these meridians.

Professor Edzard Ernst comments: 'Neither the meridians nor the acupuncture points have ever been shown to exist in an anatomical sense, nor has the existence of Yin and Yang been demonstrated convincingly'.

Given some objective evidence of limited benefit, conventional Western medical thinking has suggested 'scientific' mechanisms that might be involved: Counter irritant action is an obvious if over-simplistic suggestion. Mothers worldwide know that 'rubbing it better' helps their child's bruised knee, and the many rubefacients on the market work by 'taking your mind off' the pain underneath.

Gate theory for pain mechanisms suggests that only certain nerve signals can get in and out of the 'gate' into consciousness at any one time. On this electrophysiological model, acupuncture may exert its analgesic effect partly through the selective excitation of efferent pain inhibitory pathways. This concept might explain how a needle in one area of the body could affect another area. There is experimental evidence that endorphins and enkephalins are released in response to acupuncture. Naloxone can in most instances reverse the analgesic effects of acupuncture.

Does it work?

After a systematic review of all the available data Professor Ernst has concluded that acupuncture is of proven benefit for: nausea and vomiting, dental pain, low back pain when not caused by a specific disease. The same review approach suggests strongly that acupuncture is no more effective than sham acupuncture for: losing weight, stopping smoking.

Has acupuncture got harmful physical side-effects?

The most frequently reported adverse effects are bruising and pain felt during the needling, and (interestingly) fainting and drowsiness directly after an acupuncture session. The use of non-sterile needles may cause infections. The inevitable tissue trauma can also cause complications.

What about spiritual harm?

By associating in whatever way, however remote, with a therapy perhaps permeated by non-Christian or even anti-Christian ideology, are patients not at risk of spiritual harm? A Christian checklist:

1. Do the claims made for it fit the facts?

The 'traditional Chinese medicine' approach has seen acupuncture as a 'cure-all', for which there is no supportive evidence. Within the 'Western medical' context there is limited evidence of some objective benefit so that acupuncture may have a genuinely useful role to play.

2. Is there a rational scientific basis to the therapy?

Some suggestions have been outlined above. We must acknowledge that our understanding is currently limited, but there do seem to be some

Andrew Fergusson
wrote as CMF General Secretary

LINKS *Nucleus, October 1999. www.cmf.org.uk/publications/content.asp?context=article&id=759*

> *Medicine is a collection of uncertain prescriptions...*
> *Water, air and cleanliness are the chief*
> *articles in my pharmacopeia.*
> *Napoleon Bonaparte*

Ouch!!!

possible rational scientific explanations for the occasional benefits. It is not necessary to seek 'occult' explanations.

3. Is it the methodology or is it the principle which is the effective element?

Dr Felix Mann, former president of the British Medical Acupuncture Society wrote that 'the traditional acupuncture points are no more real than the black spots a drunkard sees in front of his eyes'. He sees no need to invoke any mystical or spiritual explanations.

4. What are the assumptions of the world view behind the therapy?

It can be understood without invoking non-Christian world views.

5. Does the therapy involve the occult?

While the therapy might not involve the occult, the therapist might! As with most if not all alternative practices the question is not so much about the nature of the therapy, but about the nature of the therapist. Who is this person I am about to place myself under?

6. Has the therapy stood the test of time?

This question is generally weaker in its diagnostic power, but applied to acupuncture, 3,500 years may suggest acupuncture has got some point!

Summary

Performed for a proper indication by a reliable practitioner (preferably medically qualified), acupuncture can be acceptable. Traditionalists using it for other indications should be avoided as of course should anything that might be occult.

ed's thoughts...

I know from much experience of discussing acupuncture that the conclusions of this article will be controversial for some. Some believers struggle to even think there might be a benefit, while other are surprised that any questions about it are raised at all. I would never advise anyone to go against their conscience, and indeed Paul's discussion of conscience and meat offered to idols in 1 Corinthians 10:14-33 may be relevant here. If you have any doubts or qualms at all, don't go for acupuncture. You probably won't miss much.

think it over...

1 A friend in church says that they are considering seeing an acupuncturist for their back pain. How would you respond?

2 How might you work out whether a particular acupuncturist was following traditional Chinese principles?

TAKE HOME MESSAGE: **There may be a scientific explanation for the few conditions in which acupuncture sometimes works**

The spine as a whole operates as a functional unit. Each vertebra can affect its neighbour and one portion of the spine may affect or damage other areas of the body.
Don Davis

CAM: Chiropractic

C hiropractic is one of the most widely used systems of alternative health care available today. The majority of consultations are for musculo-skeletal problems, particularly of the back, neck and shoulder. However, chiropractic as set out by its founder was believed to be an effective treatment for a wide range of diseases including asthma and cardiac problems; this is despite no evidence of these conditions having spinal origins.

In 1999 the World Federation of Chiropractors defined chiropractic as 'a health profession concerned with the diagnosis, treatment and prevention of mechanical disorders of the musculo-skeletal system and the effect of these disorders on the function of the nervous system and on general good health. There is an emphasis on manual treatment including spinal manipulation or adjustment.'

Origins
David Daniel Palmer (1845-1913), a Canadian grocer, originally became interested in magnetic healing and mesmerism (hypnosis). A small volume called *The Chiropractor* contains original lectures by Palmer on the principles, science, art and philosophy of chiropractic. He passionately believed that the exercise of chiropractic was a moral and religious duty, and that the spirit in man is part of the Innate Universal Intelligence, which is present in and controls our whole body. He identified this as being known to Christians as God, but it can clearly be equated to the Universal Cosmic Energy or Vital Force of many Eastern religions and alternative therapies with New Age associations. He believed that a maladjusted or displaced vertebra – subluxation – pressed on nerves, interfering with the flow of Innate Intelligence, so resulting in defective function and poor health.

The late **George Smith** wrote as a dermatologist and retired GP

Present practice
Following a medical history, chiropractic examination concentrates on posture, inspection and palpation of the spinal column. Advice regarding posture, exercise and lifestyle is given but the characteristic element of chiropractic treatment is manipulation of the spine and its associated joints, usually by high velocity/low amplitude thrusting techniques, together with massage and manipulation on specially designed tables. Vertebral adjustment by these techniques is designed to restore normal positioning and proper function. There may be an audible crack, said to be the sound of gas bubbles bursting under pressure rather than bones cracking.

Treatment by manipulation and massage has by no means been neglected by orthodox doctors and physiotherapists; it is not the prerogative of chiropractors and osteopaths. Manipulation has been advocated by physical medicine specialists (especially doctors Cyriax and Maitland) and orthopaedic surgeons, but for clearly defined and scientifically verifiable conditions. Terminology varies but doctors and physiotherapists usually define manipulation as high velocity/low amplitude techniques and describe other manipulations as manual therapy.

Does it have a rational scientific basis?
A credible and verifiable scientific basis has not been established. Palmer's original cures lack confirmation and explanation. As hearing depends on the VIII cranial nerve, vertebral adjustment of a spinal nerve is unlikely to restore hearing. Neither X-rays nor post-mortem examinations have shown reliable evidence of subluxations or their pressure effects on nerves. No verifiable scientific evidence has been produced confirming subluxations to be the cause of disease. Innate Intelligence is a spiritual or metaphysical concept, not verifiable scientifically.

LINKS

Triple Helix, Winter 2005. www.cmf.org.uk/literature/content.asp?context=article&id=1554

None of these systematic reviews demonstrate beyond reasonable doubt that chiropractic interventions are effective...
Edzard Ernst

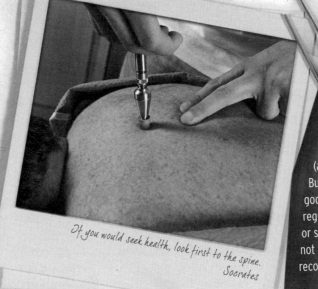

If you would seek health, look first to the spine.
Socrates

Does it work?

Hundreds of studies and more than 50 systematic reviews of published papers have been used to investigate chiropractic. Most investigations have focused on back pain and neck problems with far from convincing results. Professor Ernst, of Peninsular University, commented: 'None of these systematic reviews demonstrate beyond reasonable doubt that chiropractic interventions are effective in treating these conditions or that they are superior to other treatments – for example, physiotherapy or drugs'.

Is it safe?

Systematic reviews reveal considerable evidence of both minor and serious complications, including stroke, spinal injury, thrombosis and joint dislocations, although these are relatively uncommon. Recent studies suggest that half the patients suffered some side effects, albeit not serious. Professor Ernst states: 'Contrary to what is often said, spinal manipulation is by no means free of risk. In particular, upper spinal manipulation has been associated with serious complications.'

Conclusion

The popular view that chiropractic is a proven and safe manipulative treatment, particularly for back and neck problems, is not confirmed by detailed investigation. There is confusing and unconvincing scientific evidence for its effectiveness and serious concerns about its safety. The philosophy of chiropractic is clearly based on a non-Christian belief system, which raises important additional spiritual concerns for Christians.

ed's thoughts...

Chiropractic is popular, and much better regulated than most alternative therapies.
Many patients are sure that they benefit from it (although I've met a number who say the opposite). But it is not free of risk, nor is there particularly good evidence for it. Remember that popularity and regulation are not necessarily guarantees of efficacy or safety, and that anecdotal reports of success are not adequate evidence on which to base recommendations.

think it over...

1 On an FY2 GP placement, a patient asks if she should see the chiropractor her neighbour has recommended for her back pain. She isn't a believer. How do you respond?

2 Does your response change if the patient:
a) Suffers from osteoporosis and is on a bisphosphonate?
b) Has already tried every treatment you have to offer and is still off work?
c) Is a Christian?

think... about...

CAM: # homeopathy

Samuel Hahnemann (1755-1843) was the founder of homeopathy. He graduated in 1779 and soon became disillusioned with the ineffective, painful and sometimes fatal treatments of his day that included bloodletting, leeches, purging and medicines containing dangerous chemicals such as arsenic and mercury.

He became interested in Peruvian cinchona bark as a treatment for malaria. Having tested it on himself, he believed that small doses produced symptoms similar to those of malaria. After testing other substances, he concluded that they could be used to treat diseases with similar symptoms. He formulated his first principle of homeopathy: 'let like be cured by like'.

Hahnemann returned to medical practice and put his newfound theory into practice but with limited success. Concerned about side effects, he decided to dilute his original medicines or mother tinctures. One drop was diluted with nine or ninety nine drops of solvent (water and alcohol) making a dilution of one in ten (Ix) or one in a hundred (Ic) respectively. This process was repeated six, twelve or 30 times, eg 6c, 12c or 30c. This process of dilution is the second principle of homeopathy.

Still dissatisfied, Hahnemann decided to shake the solutions between each dilution, a process he called succussion, which he believed potentised the resulting remedy with some form of vital force. Potentisation is the third principle of homeopathy.

Although his views were generally unpopular with the medical establishment, a few doctors did accept his principles and there was a gradual worldwide spread. Homeopathic diagnosis includes a full medical history, examination and special investigations although these are necessarily restricted in those without a medical qualification. Homeopathic treatment today still

The late **George Smith** wrote as a dermatologist and retired GP

depends on Hahnemann's three original principles. The remedy may be given perhaps for six doses; if not effective, a further selection is made. If a 6c dilution does not work, a 30c strength may then be selected. It is presumed that the more extreme the dilution, the greater its efficacy.

It is commonly believed that homeopathic remedies are based only on herbs, plants and other natural substances, assuming that 'natural means harmless'. However, many of the substances in the mother tincture are noxious including anthrax poison from the spleen of an infected sheep, rattlesnake and cobra venom, discharge from a scabies blister, sulphuric acid and arsenic. But no harm results because of the extreme dilution.

Does it have a rational, scientific basis?

The idea that 'like may cure like' is contrary to orthodox medical principles. Within therapeutic limits, conventional pharmacology dictates that a higher drug concentration gives a more powerful effect. Homeopathy turns this on its head: the extreme dilutions involved mean that, from the dilutions of 12c onwards, not one molecule of substance is present in the preparation. Homeopaths do not dispute this but believe that some form of imaging or ultra molecular action takes place in the solvent during the process of potentisation. Evidence for this is not forthcoming.

Does it work?

A considerable number of scientific investigations have been attempted. A paper published in the *European Journal of Clinical Pharmacology* emphasised the difficulties encountered because there was no consensus as to the treatment in particular situations. Furthermore, the more rigorous the trial, the less likely it was to produce possible evidence

LINKS *Triple Helix, 2003. www.cmf.org.uk/literature/content.asp?context=article&id=1124*

There are no reasonable grounds for advocating homeopathy over orthodox immunisation in children.

Let like be cured by like'

in support of the homeopathic preparation. The authors stated, 'There is simply not enough evidence to conclude that homeopathy is clinically effective'.

Is it safe?
Homeopathy is often considered to be safe for minor and self-limiting complaints. A valid criticism of homeopathy is that it can encourage serious delay before seeking proven conventional treatment.

Christian Checklist
Can we, with integrity, prescribe a medicine that does not contain one molecule of effective remedy? Is it good practice to prescribe remedies that have been investigated without producing any consistent evidence of efficacy? Is it responsible to delay or withhold orthodox proven medical treatment while relying on an unproven alternative remedy? Is it acceptable to use a therapy that relies on the principle of vital force, clearly comparable with the Ch'i (yin and yang) of Eastern religions and the cosmic energy of New Age philosophies?

Summary
It is appreciated committed and zealous Christians have found homeopathy acceptable. In today's climate, it is particularly relevant for Christian doctors and nurses to decide whether or not they find homeopathy acceptable. Scientific evidence, biblical guidance and discernment from the Holy Spirit all play a part. It is my own conviction that homeopathy falls far short of being a therapy that can be acceptable to use or recommend.

ed's thoughts...

Physical harm from a highly dilute substance is very unlikely. But there must be questions about the potential harm of using a homeopathic treatment when a conventional one is desperately needed. Christians also need to question the use of a treatment which can only work if a 'vital force' is invoked. There is no reference to such a force in Scripture.

think it over...

1 Can you think of any conventional treatments with limited scientific evidence?

2 BMA is campaigning to stop NHS funding for homeopathic hospitals. Do you think the NHS should fund homeopathy?

3 Many people may see no reason why homeopathy should work, but consult a homeopath anyway. Why should this be?

TAKE HOME MESSAGE: It is hard to see any scientific basis for homeopathy, whatever our view on it spiritually

73

think...about....

CAM: reflexology

Reflexologists suggest a cause and cure relationship between minor foot abnormalities and disease of internal organs.

Reflexology, one of many touch therapies, is enjoying increasing popularity in a 'consumer led boom' in alternative medicine. It is used by 10% of alternative therapy consumers. However, Britain does not have any specific statutory regulations.

Origins
The Chinese probably used a comparable therapy some 5,000 years ago: acupressure emerged from this followed by acupuncture, which then became mainstream Chinese medicine. American ENT surgeon William Fitzgerald (1872 - 1942) applied clamps and elastic bands to fingers in order to produce arm and jaw anaesthesia, allowing him to perform minor operations. Dr Fitzgerald devised a theory that the body was divided into ten vertical zones or slices ending in the five fingers and toes on each side. No explanation is recorded as to how he reached this conclusion. In the 1930s, Eunice Ingham (1879 - 1974) – an associate of Fitzgerald – produced extremely detailed maps of reflex areas representing all parts of the body on the hands and feet.

Principles and practice
Reflexology is presented as a holistic therapy in which pressure and massage are applied to the feet or hands in order to remove and dissipate energy blocks, break down crystalline structures, encourage toxin release, stimulate the immune system and prevent ill health. Reflexologists do not claim to make medical diagnoses but identify body parts that are 'out of balance' and require removal of energy blocks. A medical history is supplemented by information gained by foot palpation. Areas of grittiness or tenderness are presumed to identify organs relating to the reflex area or zone involved. Massage, pressure or techniques such as finger walking across the foot are used to unblock energy channels, stimulate vital energy and promote healing. Individual reflexologists may combine this with colour therapy, yoga, aromatherapy, homeopathy or astrology.

Feeling better does not imply healing

Is there a rational, scientific basis?
There does not appear to be a rational basis for Dr Fitzgerald's theory of body zones. Any significant anatomical or physiological relationships between the variously shaped body organs and his geometric vertical segments or reflex areas on the foot are hard to imagine and quite incompatible with *Gray's Anatomy*. Different practitioners' foot maps have similar patterns but show clear variations in the positioning of certain organs. No convincing explanation for these variations has been offered.

Diagnosis of blocked energy channels – said to be causing crystalline deposits – by foot palpation is not backed up by scientific investigation or evidence. In New Age settings, a query over whether this is diagnosis or divination must be raised. Life force, vital energy, meridians and chakras all figure prominently in popular reflexology textbooks.

Does it work?
Reflexology is popular: its practitioners are enthusiastic and caring and many patients testify to its positive effects. A soothing foot massage in a caring environment may well diminish stress and patients often feel better. Yet anecdotal evidence and acknowledgement of the placebo effect cannot substitute for scientific evidence. Feeling better does not automatically imply healing from disease.

The late **George Smith** wrote as a dermatologist and retired GP

LINKS *Triple Helix 2003. www.cmf.org.uk/literature/content.asp?context=article&id=1166*

Make your feet your friend.
JM Barrie

Is it safe?

Significant harm seems unlikely from simple foot massage but foot tenderness, changes in micturition or bowel function have been reported. Caution is advised in patients suffering from depression, epilepsy or vascular disorders of the legs. The greatest risk is when reflexology is used as a substitute for proper medical diagnosis and treatment.

Christian checklist

Christians need to consider both professional integrity and biblical guidelines when assessing any treatment, orthodox or alternative. Unproven effectiveness or mode of action causes reflexology to fall far short of the evidence-based principles supposedly required of all modern medical treatments.

From a Christian perspective there is much to cause concern. Reflexologists highlight the spiritual significance of healing through the feet. Inge Dougans comments: 'Feet play a significant part in spiritual well being. The feet connect us to the ground and they are therefore a connection between earthly and spiritual life. They are our base and foundation and our contact with the energies that flow through it.' Many other reflexologists find an association with chakras and elements of the Hindu practice of yoga. The Christian worldview is of a personal Father God upon whom we depend in all aspects of our life. The idea of an impersonal life force governing all living beings is contrary to this and must surely lead to the conclusion that reflexology is not a right choice for Christians.

ed's thoughts...

Although relatively safe in itself, reflexology has no rational or scientific basis and randomised controlled trials show no evidence of its efficacy. As with homeopathy, there is a risk that essential conventional treatment could be delayed if reflexology is sought first. Patients may feel more relaxed after reflexology treatment, which explain why some find it helpful. But such benefits do not mean that there is a medical basis for it.

think it over...

1 You meet someone over coffee after church who works in reflexology. What might you want to ask her?

2 You work in palliative care as an ST1, and are asked for your thoughts on adding reflexology to the department's complementary therapies programme. What would you say?

TAKE HOME MESSAGE: **Reflexology may appear medically safe, but may not be spiritually safe**

Psychiatry as a profession

It is more important to know what sort of person has a disease than to know what sort of disease a person has.
Hippocrates

The call to a purposeful future is one of the blessings of being a Christian. Some usefully think of mission as being general ministry direction ('to be like Jesus', 'to help build his kingdom', 'to know him and make him known' etc) and vision as being the specific, individual task which God has for a person or group.

It is exciting to realise that our everyday work can be our vision. Psychiatry is as much a vocation as full time pastoral ministry. With God's grace, a Christian psychiatrist in the NHS can be as much involved in frontline Christian service as any cross-cultural missionary.

Christians in psychiatry can make some unique contributions:

- Truly holistic assessment and management of patients due to an appreciation of relevant spiritual factors
- Dealing with Christian patients who may be more comfortable seeing a skilled practitioner who also understands their faith
- Liaison with other helpers who may have a spiritual input into the care of the patient, if appropriate
- Facilitating better understanding and co-operation between mental health services and the church
- Playing a part in incorporating true spirituality into the healthcare arena through research and evidence-based practice

Philosophy of ministry

All truth is God's truth and it is wholly biblical to welcome science as the systematic discovery of factual truth created by God but not directly revealed in his Word. We need not fear psychopharmacology or psychoanalysis if we have openness to all God's truth coupled with an ability to discern falsehood. The Bible sees the human predicament in the context of spiritual warfare.

Ken Yeow wrote as a psychiatric registrar

Illness and suffering are the consequences of a spoiled creation where the workings of a personal evil, the sinful nature of man and a corrupt world system are evident in distorted biology, broken relationships and deep insecurity. For the Christian, the practice of psychiatry can reflect the wider kingdom ministry of healing the broken-hearted and setting the captives free; one of the fundamental objectives of the gospel.

There is much to figure out both in theory and in practice; we need wisdom and boldness

We have tremendous resources available to do God's work. The indwelling Holy Spirit is our greatest help as we seek to minister healing and restoration. The word of God is the truth that can unlock darkened minds. Prayer can bring life to disturbed souls. In the church, we potentially have a model for the community and meaningful relationships that some believe are at the heart of emotional healing.

We need to extend the traditional biopsychosocial framework into a biopsychosociospiritual one. The extra dimension is relevant to diagnosis, aetiology and treatment. The spirituality we are primarily interested in is biblical; so we need to beware of wholly absorbing the various philosophies of postmodern society.

An approach to people

Our work is about impacting people's lives for the gospel. Discipleship involves pre-evangelism, evangelism and edification and a good place to start is by learning to see people through the eyes of Jesus; every contact with a patient (or relative or colleague) then becomes an

LINKS *Triple Helix*, Autumn 2003. www.cmf.org.uk/literature/content.asp?context=article&id=1165

Psychiatry literally means 'the medical treatment of the mind'.

Mad, bad or sad?

opportunity to be a channel of blessing from God to that individual. In dealing with non-believers, we need to go about our business in such a way as to make others wonder about the positive difference in our lives. In the process of helping people work through their problems, we can introduce concepts that reflect deeper truth and eternal matters.

I am stirred up when I meet Christian patients and find myself adopting a much more open stance faith-wise. Some people are genuinely seeking the Lord for answers and it becomes a privilege to help them discover a missing kernel of truth. Others may have fallen away and there may be a chance to help draw them back into the fold.

Difficulties and dilemmas

We need to guard against unrealistic expectations about what can be achieved in an essentially secular setting. We must also avoid being overzealous with our faith – 'conventional treatments' may often be the very best. Occasionally, the only and appropriate thing to do is commit someone to the Lord in prayer as we disengage therapeutically.

If we see our secular work as our ministry then we need to expect the kind of opposition that committed Christian service incites. It is important to realise that we do not wrestle against flesh and blood. We need to be ever careful in our personal walk and utterly obedient to the leading of the Spirit.

think it over...

1 How often do you deal with patients with mental illness, even if not a psychiatrist?

2 What worries you about dealing with psychiatric patients?

3 What questions might help you find out if a mental illness has a spiritual dimension?

4 One of your patients has a spiritual problem which you feel ill-equipped to handle. The rest of your team are not Christians. Who else could help the patient, and what could they do for them?

TAKE HOME MESSAGE: **Psychiatry brings opportunities for Christians, not just problems**

Christians in research

When every activity is understood as making, then every situation into which we act is seen as raw material, waiting to have something made out of it
Oliver O'Donovan

Research has long been regarded as an aid to advancement in medicine. It is therefore not surprising that individuals have been tempted to falsify the reports of their research, given the increasingly competitive nature of medical careers. A study of the attitudes of 194 newly appointed consultants to research fraud found that 55.7% claimed to have witnessed research misconduct while 5.7% admitted to personal misconduct in research. When asked whether they would perpetrate misconduct in research in the future, 18.7% either agreed that they would or were unsure if they would. Fraudulent reporting of research can harm patients and can lead to a waste of resources.

A Christian attitude

Are there any specifically Christian considerations over and above the basic requirement of integrity that is expected of all medical practitioners? To put it another way – why should Christians be involved in research and how should they conduct themselves in it?

The Lord Jesus taught us that the greatest commandment was, 'Love the Lord your God with all your heart, and with all your soul, and with all your mind, and with all your strength'. The assumption that Christianity is anti-intellectual is as far from the truth as it possibly could be. We are called upon to use our minds as part of our worship. God has given us curiosity, and we honour him when we seek to understand the world around us. Research is a channelling and refining of that natural curiosity to make it more effective and productive.

If the first command is to love God, the second is 'Love your neighbour as yourself'. Acting in the best interest of our patients means providing them with the best evidence

based management. In order to meet our patients' needs effectively we must be familiar with the latest science and technology.

We are called to be salt and light in this world applying the highest standards to planning, conduct and reporting of research, and to others

How should we conduct ourselves?

Diligently – Every Christian's primary duty is to God but this should show itself in the way we approach our everyday lives. No task should be routine or unimportant because we are told, 'Whatever you do work at it with all your heart, as working for the Lord' (Colossians 3:23). This applies to our approach to research as well as everything else. Good research requires hard work and attention to detail.

Honestly – Jesus himself exhorted us to be both plain and trustworthy in what we say. Christians are called to follow the one who is the truth; that must mean the truthful reporting of our findings, whether or not they support our cherished hypotheses.

With humility – Humility should be a defining characteristic of our lives as Christians. Our value in God's eyes does not depend on our cleverness or our discoveries. If God has called us to research and given us the talents necessary to be successful in this field, then we must follow that calling faithfully but not think that it makes us in any way superior to others whose calling is different.

Sam Leinster wrote as Dean of the University of East Anglia School of Medicine

LINKS *Triple Helix, 2007. www.cmf.org.uk/literature/content.asp?context=article&id=1908*

Get wisdom. Though it cost all you have, get understanding. Cherish her, and she will exalt you; embrace her, and she will honour you.
Proverbs 4: 7-8

testimony

Helen says... Many Christian doctors see their principal role as working on the 'frontline' with patients. Yet for others, it is a privilege to work behind the scenes, discovering more about the way God created us, and translating this to help patients in the future. However, academia brings its own set of challenges.

The research world is notoriously competitive, and I suspect that's particularly true amongst medics. From our school days we are used to being amongst the top achievers, then at medical school competition increases for everything from exam prizes to the best FY1 jobs.

It's easy to fall into the competitiveness of academia: feeling a sense of smugness at having a few more publications... an abstract from an international conference... that prestigious job... At the end of the day it's God who's put me here, who's given me both the opportunities and the skills to do what I love doing. I just hope I never lose hold of that.

God has given us curiosity

Philippians 2:3 **Do nothing out of selfish ambition or vain conceit, but in humility consider others better than yourselves.**

TAKE HOME MESSAGE: **The more we understand of the way things work, the greater will be our understanding of God**

think it over...

1 Think about integrity in the following areas of Work:
a) Correct clinical details on radiology request cards
b) Sickness certification
c) Explaining to a consultant why something hasn't been done

2 Have you ever witnessed poor research ethics?

3 How would you advise a fellow doctor who had noticed their consultant falsifying research findings?

O will use treatments for the benefit of the ill in accordance with my ability and my judgement
The Hippocratic Oath

Conscientious OBJECTION

The right of conscientious objection is enshrined in medical law, but is increasingly coming under attack from a number of prominent ethicists and writers. Professor Julian Savalescu, a well-known bioethicist, has said that 'A doctor's conscience has little place in the delivery of modern medical care'.

A recent article in the *New England Journal of Medicine* stated: 'As the gate-keepers to medicine, physicians and other health care providers have an obligation to choose specialties that are not moral minefields for them'.

The practice of medicine requires moral integrity
It is often assumed that the role of the conscience in medicine is relevant only to a few specialised and limited areas such as abortion or contraception. But in fact the concept of the conscience goes right to the heart of what it means to act in a moral way, with integrity.

Doctors are not just paid artisans who do whatever their paymasters require. They are not just civil servants whose first loyalty is to the state. They are not just salesmen whose job is to keep the customers satisfied.

Ever since Hippocrates, the practice of medicine has been founded in a number of core ethical values. Practising good medicine is a moral and not just a technical activity. The foundational values of medicine are part of physicians' understanding of who they are and they have provided the basis for historical codes of medical ethics, such as the Hippocratic Oath, the Declaration of Geneva and the General Medical Council's *Good Medical Practice*. Moral commitments of the doctor from *Good Medical Practice* include:

John Wyatt
wrote as Professor of
Ethics and Perinatology

- Make the care of your patient your first concern
  - Protect and promote the health of patients and the public
    - Provide a good standard of practice and care

- Treat patients as individuals and respect their dignity
- Work in partnership with patients
- Be honest and open and act with integrity

These core ethical values become part of the physician's understanding of who they are and what they have entered medicine for. They are central to the doctor's self-identity. And when a person is coerced by employers, or by the power of the state, to act in a way which transgresses these core ethical values then their internal moral integrity is damaged.

Examples of the corruption of medicine
Over the last century there have been many startling and egregious cases when the core ethical commitments of medicine have been corrupted and violated. Misuse of psychiatry in Stalinist Russia and the barbaric experiments in Nazi Germany are well documented.

We must not be naïve in thinking that medical practice cannot become morally corrupted. History teaches us that when doctors are subject to coercion from state power or other sources, they may act in ways which deny the fundamental moral values of good medicine. It is an essential safeguard for the moral health of medicine that legal and regulatory systems are maintained which protect the rights of doctors to refuse to take part in practices which violate their most profound moral convictions.

Christian thinking about the conscience
In biblical thinking, the conscience is one of the most fundamental aspects of what it means to be a human being. The conscience is part of our created humanity and it is present in all, not just those who are

LINKS *CMF File, 2009. admin.cmf.org.uk/pdf/cmffiles/39_doctors_conscience.pdf*

Good medicine depends on good moral choices

Personal beliefs can sometimes cause conflicts

believers. The conscience is seen as, in some sense, an internal reflection of God's law for all mankind. The Apostle Paul, writing of the Gentiles who did not receive the Mosaic law, states that 'what the law requires is written on their hearts'.

But the human conscience as an internal moral compass is not an infallible guide to morality. As fallen human beings our consciences are inevitably corrupted and contaminated by evil. It is possible for human beings to reach a point in which their conscience becomes completely insensitive. So the teaching of the New Testament is that the conscience needs to be constantly instructed, informed and re-aligned by Christian truth.

Conclusion

The right of conscientious objection is not a minor or peripheral issue. It goes to the heart of medical practice as a moral activity. Current UK law and professional guidelines respect the right of doctors to refuse to engage in certain procedures to which they have a conscientious objection. However, the right of conscience is not absolute and doctors have a duty to preserve the best interests of their patients and to keep them fully informed.

The right of conscience helps to preserve the moral integrity of the individual clinician, preserves the distinctive characteristics and reputation of medicine as a profession, acts as a safeguard against coercive state power, and provides protection from discrimination for those with minority ethical beliefs.

ed's thoughts...

GMC guidance on Personal Beliefs and Medical Practice (2008) states that 'All doctors have personal beliefs which affect their day-to-day practice. Some doctors' personal beliefs may give rise to concerns about carrying out or recommending particular procedures for patients.'

It goes on to say that 'Patients may ask you to perform, advise on, or refer them for a treatment or procedure which is not prohibited by law or statutory code of practice in the country where you work, but to which you have a conscientious objection. In such cases you must tell patients of their right to see another doctor with whom they can discuss their situation and ensure that they have sufficient information to exercise that right.'

Simply put, the GMC recognises conscientious objection as valid, but is clear that it must be exercised carefully.

think it over...

1 What issues other than abortion or euthanasia might give rise to conscientious objection for the Christian?

2 How would you explain a conscientious objection to abortion to another doctor who has to see the patients whom you don't refer?

3 How might you explain your objections to a non-Christian patient who had expected an abortion referral?

THINK 26 · think....about....

discrimination

There have never been so many old people in our society. Nor have people ever lived (on average) so long. Although Europe is now the 'oldest' continent, the greatest percentage-rise in elderly people is occurring in the developing world. The numbers of very elderly people (80 and over) in the UK will nearly double in the next five to ten years.

Traditionally, our society has not valued elderly people very highly. This has been particularly true in the last few decades where youth and freshness have taken precedence over experience and wisdom. Middle-aged persons, not just elderly men and women, have found themselves having a crisis of identity. Many feel less than useful, unsure of their niche in society.

Dealing with dying

The problem of intensity of treatment as life approaches its end requires the wisdom of Solomon and the kindness that reflects the compassion of our Heavenly Father. This is immensely challenging and often painful for those concerned. Finding out what old people really want for themselves means time at the bedside, and that means not going to useless meetings or filling our lives, as healthcare professionals, with paperwork and committees.

Dying elderly people are the most unwelcome to many of our colleagues – and perhaps the ones we should be most seen with. The Lord spent his time with the real and social lepers of his day. Living prophetically in this way will cost us, both in time and probably also in prestige.

Christians themselves often need to come to terms with their own mortality, whatever their head-knowledge of the resurrection and heaven. How will Christian healthcare professionals fare in the bewildering speed of change? How do you feel adequate in the face of large amounts of unmet need?

Mark Cheesman wrote as a consultant geriatrician

People in God's image

Compassion and kindness are a language the deaf can hear and the blind can see. People around us need to see Jesus in us. There is no substitute for spending time in God's presence so we can reflect him. The only way we as Christian doctors will spend time in our heavenly Father's presence is by timetabling it in.

Treating elderly people as beings made in God's image involves more than just showing clinical competence

The Bible says that there is a tragic grandeur about us: we are immortal beings made for our Creator and forever unsatisfied without him. It teaches that God so loved us that he sent his Son Jesus to be one of us, talk with us, teach us, die for us and rise again: so that we could not only walk with him in this world but rise from the dead and be in his presence for eternity. And the Bible assures us that, inadequate as we are, we can bring the grace and presence of God to each other. Old people are often kind, patient, and understanding: and often delighted to interact with us if only we will slow down to be with them. The Christian concept of seeing the Lord in other people and caring for them out of love for him is a powerful driver for good, if we will embrace it.

Triple Helix, 2001. www.cmf.org.uk/literature/content.asp?context=article&id=1038

testimony

Ranti says... Despite having experienced it on a number of occasions, discrimination always takes me by surprise. In the context of being a doctor, it is often subtle and hard to quantify but still leaves a bitter aftertaste. As a female black, discrimination is fact.

The incident that most stands out for me is when a blind patient, who I had been managing, refused any further treatment once he found out that I was black. How do you handle this? As a professional you have to make sure the person is still treated appropriately, even if that means getting another doctor. As a Christian you do have to actively practise love and forgiveness – not easy, but necessary if bitterness is not going to take root. At times it is appropriate to fight it, particularly if you see discrimination towards someone else. Most importantly, defining your identity in Christ, enjoying that he made me, is the best way to remove the bitter aftertaste.

Jeremy says... Even as a white English male, racism can be apparent. I did my GP registrar post in a deprived, largely white-populated urban area. I was the only white doctor in the practice much of the time – and occasionally came across patients who referred to this. Some just implicitly mentioned the fact, but a few were clearer that they were seeing me because of my skin colour.

It wasn't always easy to challenge. Even pointing out that the permanent GPs had all grown up locally (and that I hadn't) didn't usually help. Those I did challenge often took it badly, expecting the 'white doctor' to be on their side. Some that I didn't challenge were difficult patients where medical care and communication were problematic enough.

Often it was a matter of prioritising – challenging the patients where appropriate, but more often accepting that I had to just get on with providing their medical care, respecting their right to hold views I disagreed with.

Learn the language of compassion

ed's thoughts...

This page deals with two distinct forms of discrimination. The main article looks at a common situation in which patients are discriminated against, and Jeremy's testimony considers discrimination by patients, against other doctors.

Ranti's testimony deals with much more direct experience, when she herself was the person discriminated against - a difficult and more testing situation.

Whatever form discrimination may take, it cannot be defended when all people, regardless of age, race or gender, are made in God's image.

think it over...

1 How might you explain an age limit (for example upper age limits in cervical screening) to a patient? Can such limits ever be justified?

2 What changes can you make during your working day to give elderly patients the time they need?

3 What should you say to a patient who refuses to see your colleague from overseas on racial grounds? Is such a request any different from a request to see a doctor of a particular gender? If so, why? How about someone who explicitly requests a Christian doctor?

fallibility

As a doctor as well as a human being, there will be occasions when you fall short. You may make an error of judgment; you might miss something, or maybe you will fail to do something you should do. Occasionally, your mistake may not be correctable. Accepting the fallibility of human nature is likely to be a huge protective factor against bad practice.

None of us is perfect

Christian medical personnel can find themselves in a double bind: you're part of the 'no errors allowed' medical culture and your Christian tradition says 'Be perfect therefore!' Church preaching and teaching often suggest, sometimes explicitly, that Christians should be better than other people. Yet we know from experience that none of us is perfect. None of us lives without faults and mistakes.

Among the many cries of delight greeting the recent birth of my new granddaughter was, 'Oh, she's perfect!' Of course, this doesn't mean that she won't make mistakes or that we expect her to be a saint. Rather, it means that we rejoice in her wholeness. She has everything she needs to have a go at life.

Be whole and fit for purpose

The biblical commentators give a variety of interpretations of Matthew 5:48: 'Be perfect, therefore, as your heavenly Father is perfect'. They are all agreed that moral perfection is impossible for human beings; and point out that the gospels also assume this. They also agree that the word translated as 'perfect' has a wide scope with strands of meaning encompassing 'wholeness' and 'fitness for purpose'. So, actually, its meaning is closer to our

Annie Hargrave wrote as a psychotherapist at InterHealth in London

cry of delight over a new baby than the stern demand for unachievable Old Testament perfection which lives so doggedly in many people's consciences.

If we substitute 'Be whole and fit for purpose...' for 'Be perfect...' then Matthew 5:48 opens up a more humane challenge for living.

Be whole – Don't pretend, hide, shut things out or blame others inappropriately. Accept yourself and allow forgiveness and mercy to yourself as well as to others. Look after yourself, body, mind and spirit.

Seeking supportive colleagues and putting supportive structures in place can enhance good practice and keep you open to ongoing learning and development

Be fit for purpose – this is the challenge to professionalism: be well trained, expanding your skills and applying yourself to the hard work involved so that you grow to be more and more 'fit for purpose'. It is also the challenge to the way we live our lives in every part: our prayer life, our friendships and families, our business dealings, our compassion, our bodies, our 'whole'. So then, as the biblical commentators highlight, we will be 'fit for purpose' in the sense that we are in the best place to seek God.

LINKS *Triple Helix, 2007. www.cmf.org.uk/literature/content.asp?context=article&id=1946*

Caroline says... I found the transition from medical student to doctor fraught with stress. In particular, I struggled with the responsibility I had for patients. If I made a mistake, I carried around a burden of guilt, and became even more fearful of causing harm. This led to an increasing difficulty in making management decisions. After a short period of sick leave I resigned, and haven't worked in clinical medicine since.

In my experience Christian doctors may be especially susceptible to excessive conscientiousness. If counselling a friend in this situation I would now tell them to be less critical of themselves, hand over their fears to the Lord, and trust him who is sovereign, rather than taking personal responsibility for everything. These were the very things that at the time I was unable to do.

In the years since, I have started to understand my personality better, and discovered frailties I never knew I had. This self-knowledge has led to a more realistic view of myself; I am learning to cut myself some slack, and let God be God. Wonderfully, his grace is sufficient. He has taken me in new directions that I could not have foreseen, and uses me in spite of, and sometimes through, my weaknesses.

Lucy says... My bleep goes off in the middle of the ward round - 'This is the complaints department...' The scenario: a gentlemen sent home from A&E with a headache (by myself and seniors), then readmitted and diagnosed with a subarachnoid haemorrhage. He now, understandably, wanted to know what had gone wrong, and written accounts were required.

My first response was to feel defensive, was it my fault? Then set in the fear, guilt, embarrassment and total loss of confidence. I spoke to close colleagues and friends, and brought the situation to God. It was difficult, but a big learning experience: admitting I could make mistakes, facing them with honesty, and moving on to try and do things better. I felt reassured that if I desired to do God's will, he could use me despite my mistakes. I realised afresh the importance of loving my patients as God would, and therefore treating them to the best of my ability.

Accept yourself

1 John 2:12 **I am writing to you, dear children, because your sins have been forgiven on account of his name.**

think it over...

Think about your instinctive responses to these questions.

1 How do they compare with the 'correct' responses you feel you are sometimes expected to give?

2 What do you do when you notice someone else making a mistake?

3 What do you do when you make a mistake?

4 How do you think medical mistakes should be acted on?

5 What do you do when a patient can no longer be helped by medicine?

think... about...

gospel ministry

How beautiful on the mountains are the feet of those
who bring good news,
Isaiah 52:7

A **medical student thinking through his career options told me recently,** 'The overriding need in this world is for people to hear the gospel; therefore the only thing worth doing with my life, if I am able, is to become an ordained minister'.

For me this begs important questions; for example, what proportion of the time of an ordained minister actually involves evangelism, direct or indirect? But the issues go deeper than that. Many will intuitively sense that something is awry with my friend's statement. How does one respond theologically to what can seem for many a powerful argument?

Evangelism is undoubtedly the logical priority of Christianity. A question for me is this: does this make it our only responsibility? It is our Saviour's intention that our whole lives, our worship, might reflect God's sovereign rule over every area of life – as salt sustaining, light shining agents of his common grace in the world. We are created 'to do good works' as well as to be agents of his saving grace through Christ. As John Stott has suggested, 'We have all been prodigals; God wants us all to be Samaritans too'.

Loving our neighbours

Jesus tells us that The Law can be summarised in the two commands to love God and to love our neighbour. And as the parable of the Good Samaritan shows, our neighbour is simply anyone in need, made in the image of God. Practically, Jesus demonstrated this in his actions as he 'went round teaching' and 'went around doing good and healing'.

As with Jesus' ministry, the expression of this love over a period of time should rarely be less than evangelism, but will undoubtedly involve other areas of service as our

Jason Roach wrote as a medically qualified ministry apprentice

individual gifts and opportunities are carefully weighed and reweighed throughout our lives. They are partners not enemies.

Social responsibility is a biblical requirement, but can also be a bridge to evangelism, by removing prejudices, and opening doors that were previously closed

Making choices

As doctors, we will want to see God's will done in many different spheres: bioethics, health care rationing, global health or faithful preaching. All these need people uniquely gifted to serve in their particular fields.

We do need to make life choices carefully in full submission, prayerfully, with wise counsel and with our minds. However, we need to remember that nothing we can do can affect the plan of he who 'works out everything in conformity with the purpose of his will'.

Even if we make what we think is the 'wrong' choice, God will use us to effect his plans if we submit ourselves to his will. This means that it is unhelpful to think of the offices of teacher or preacher or missionary or doctor or nurse as 'rankable' in terms of import in the eyes of the Lord. Our task is in whatever we do, wherever we are, to 'work at it with all your heart, as working for the Lord, not for men... It is the Lord Christ you are serving' (Colossians 3:23-24).

LINKS *Triple Helix, 2004. www.cmf.org.uk/literature/content.asp?context=article&id=1267*

We have all been prodigals: God wants us all to be Samaritans too.
John Stott

testimony

Laurence says... Knowing what to do halfway into a year out of medicine as a part-time intern with CMF wasn't easy. I was really enjoying the year – and not missing medicine at all. I was moving to another part of the country to get married at the end of the year and needed the resources to do this, hence the need for a 'job' of some description. Medicine was the only thing I was really trained for.

Looking back it's easier to understand why it was probably right for me to continue in medicine at the time. Having only worked as a house officer (the old equivalent of FY1), I wouldn't have been able to make much use of my medical training in any other field at that stage. I would not have gone on to have the opportunities to serve God that I now enjoy in a varied career currently encompassing general practice, prison medicine and ministry with CMF.

What I do changes from day to day. The skills I use in a prison clinic differ from those needed in a normal general practice surgery. When at CMF, I might be editing an article one morning, organising a conference that afternoon, and speaking at a meeting in the evening.

I know that I cannot possibly have the 'perfect' set of gifts to do all these things – but also know that there are many more ways God can use me in a varied working life – probably far more than if I had gone to theological college!

Work for the Lord, not men

Ephesians 2:10 **For we are God's workmanship, created in Christ Jesus to do good works, which God prepared in advance for us to do.**

think it over...

1 What opportunities does a doctor have to serve God a pastor does not?

2 Is there a divide between the 'secular' and the 'sacred' in your life?

3 If you did feel a strong calling to leave medicine, how might you test it?

4 Have you considered working part-time in medicine and part-time in a ministry role?

5 Might this be an option for you?

TAKE HOME MESSAGE: **The Lord cares less where we serve him, but that we serve him, with everything, and in everything**

Harm reduction

Should we participate in treatments that aim to reduce harm, but may also enable or encourage acts we consider to be wrong? This is an area where Christians don't always agree. Here we present two different views:

VIEW ONE

You are a school doctor on your way out of school after a busy drop-in clinic. A sixteen-year-old girl called Katie approaches you. She tells you that she and her boyfriend Tom have decided to sleep together tonight (rarely is first sexual intercourse in young people so premeditated or rational). In their haste she forgot to discuss contraception, she knows Tom would be useless at remembering and asks whether you can help her by supplying a condom.

I will now set out the arguments to support my conviction that it would never be right to supply her with a condom, based on what the Bible says about sin – its consequences and the role of a Christian in deterring sinful actions. Some of my conclusions may seem impossibly demanding to our everyday practice. However, when you absorb the full implications of the practice and consequences of the so-called 'harm reduction' approach, I hope you will see the great need for a very different, and, I believe, biblical alternative.

If I accept that Katie has moral responsibility for her plan to have sex, what are the options available to me?

There seem to be two main aims I might pursue:
Aim A. To deter her from her sinful plans.
Aim B. To protect her from the unwanted consequences of having sex – of what we recognise as a sinful act.

Now let's briefly identify some biblical perspectives that might inform these aims:

Chris Richards wrote as a Consultant Paediatrician and **Peter May** wrote as a GP

Aim A: Should we deter people from sinning?

- God lays down commands for us to obey (Deuteronomy 5:32)
- His commands reflect his character (Psalm 19:7-10)
- God's commands are for both Christian and non-Christian (Romans 3:19)
- We are accountable to God for influencing the sin of others (Matthew 18:6)
- And for what we do and what we don't do (James 4:17)

As within our influence and opportunity, we are called by God to dissuade people from sinning.

Aim B: Should we soften the consequences of future sin?

- Actions have consequences such as the events following David's adultery with Bathsheba (2 Samuel 11), or the harvest of a godly life.
- Bad consequences of sin are contrasted with the good consequences of obedience (Deuteronomy 28).
- God warns us of the bad consequences of disobedience in order to encourage us to obey. Jesus warned the healed invalid, 'stop sinning or something worse may happen to you' (John 5:14).
- Denial of sin's consequences is a ploy of the Evil One to encourage us to sin.
- God uses the consequences of sin to draw people back to himself and the softening of their consequences as a sign of his compassion (2 Samuel 12:13).
- Nowhere in the Bible does God reassure us that in anticipation of sinning, we can expect the consequences to be softened nor does the Bible give Christians any mandate to do so.

In summary, we may have an opportunity to warn Katie that her plans are sinful and will have bad consequences. However, in anticipation of a sinful act, we must not 'aid and abet' sin nor soften its consequences by supplying her with the condom. More positively, we may have the opportunity to encourage her to see the goodness of God's ways by keeping sex until the committed relationship of marriage.

LINKS

Material is drawn from both: Triple Helix, 2003. www.cmf.org.uk/literature/content.asp?context=article&id=1163
Triple Helix, 2004. www.cmf.org.uk/literature/content.asp?context=article&id=1180

29

*We are called to follow the one who rolled up
his sleeves and got alongside them.*
Peter May

VIEW TWO

There are a few — mainly girls in their teens — who come for contraceptive advice before embarking on a sexual relationship. If she has not been prescribed contraception before, I ask about her intentions. Mostly, she has made her mind up already. Early in my career, I thought naively that I could persuade a young woman to change her mind: she returned within a few weeks requesting a termination.

Now, when my advice is called for, I ask my patient to listen very carefully: 'I will say this only once!' If after reflection, she still wants to embark on a sexual relationship, and returns for contraception, I will prescribe it without further discussion unless she initiates it. Often, these young women then go to a Youth Advisory Clinic instead and change to another GP. The doctor-patient relationship is easily destroyed.

What do I tell them? With gentle irony, I point out that there is a close, scientifically proven, correlation between intercourse and having babies, and no contraception is 100% reliable. Of course, I warn of the risks of diverse infections. I point out the emotional dangers of multiple relationships, which statistically decrease the likelihood of entering into an enduring relationship in the future. I even talk about the wonderful joy and confidence that can be experienced in a unique relationship for life.

However, 99% of these young women have already begun a sexual relationship, so providing them with contraception is hardly facilitating their sin. My task is one of damage limitation. If they become pregnant, there is a very high risk they will have the pregnancy terminated. I would sooner that life was not created than that it should be destroyed. I don't want them to get herpes, warts, chlamydia, cervical carcinoma or something even worse! Therefore, I teach them about these risks and

It's a messy old world!

encourage them to use condoms, which I provide if requested.

Consequentialism *per se* is a totally inadequate system for moral decision making but woe betide the Christian who seeks to understand God's will without regard for consequences! They have to be taken into account.

It is a messy old world. People can behave appallingly but we are called to follow one who rolled up his sleeves and got alongside them. Jesus didn't come to condemn the world but to save it and taught that judgment was God's business and not ours. As guilty sinners, who have found God's forgiveness, we should not be overly preoccupied with our own moral purity. Jesus rebuked the Pharisees who tied heavy loads on people's shoulders and did not lift a finger to help them. He also told the story of the priest who, to protect his own purity, walked by on the other side, leaving a Samaritan outcast to rescue a dying man. Much misunderstood, Jesus became the friend of sinners. He helped without bullying them or overriding their decisions. Such was his identification with lost people that he became sin for us and died on a cross for our redemption.

think it over...

1 What might be the adverse effects of not giving contraception in these circumstances?

2 What might be the adverse effects of giving contraception?

3 Having considered the effect, are we correct in deciding our course of action by balancing its apparent good and bad consequences (known as utilitarianism)?

4 How do we honour God when an assessment of consequences seems to conflict with Biblical commands?

JW'S + BlOOd

Now that faith has come, we are no longer under the supervision of the law.
Galatians 3:25

The Jehovah's Witness movement was founded in 1884, in the United States, by Charles Taze Russell. Russell, reputedly a compelling speaker, had previously been a member of a conventional Christian church but then found reasons to disagree with much of its theology. The movement, originally known as Zion's Watchtower Society, preaches a literal belief in the Bible, aided by Russell's own 'Aid to Bible Understanding'. Whilst originally basing their doctrines on the King James Version, in 1961 they introduced their own version, 'The New World Translation of the Holy Scriptures', with significant alterations from other, accepted translations. They deny, among other things, the Trinity, the personage of the Holy Spirit, the deity of Christ, bodily resurrection and a visible Second Coming. They represent one of the largest sects in the world today, publishing more material than all the other world sects combined.

The prohibition of blood transfusions was introduced by the Society towards the end of World War II. Its introduction was a relatively gradual process and followed prior objections to vaccination, inoculation and organ transplantation. (Since the 1950s acceptance of these treatments has been left up to the individual's conscience.) The first direct mention of the prohibition was in 1944: 'Not only as a descendant of Noah, but now also as one bound by God's law to Israel which incorporated the everlasting covenant regarding the sanctity of life-sustaining blood, the stranger was forbidden to eat or drink blood, whether by transfusion or by the mouth'.

Jehovah's Witnesses argue that transfusion involves the use of blood as a nutrient and base their objection to it on three biblical passages forbidding blood ingestion: Genesis 9:4, Leviticus 17:11-14 and Acts 15:20, 29.

Anne Sanderson wrote as a medical secretary and **Mandi Fry** wrote as a medical student.

But both Genesis 9:4 and Leviticus 17:11-14 clearly relate to the blood of animals and birds killed for food or sacrifice and make no mention of human blood. Similarly in Acts 15:20, 29, the Jerusalem Council's edict to 'abstain from...blood' makes no suggestion that human blood is being implicated. Furthermore this was a command primarily aimed at maintaining peace between early Christians from Jewish and Gentile backgrounds.

Clinicians need to know what's really going on so they can ensure that Jehovah's Witness patients make independent choices

Christians are not under Mosaic Law today (see Galatians 3:23-25; Colossians 2:13-15) but even in the Old Testament the punishment for blood ingestion was not excommunication, but simply to bathe and wait until evening when one would be considered 'clean' (Leviticus 17:15,16). The Jehovah's Witnesses position is not biblically defensible.

Under the Old Covenant blood shed in animal sacrifices was sacred, epitomising the life of the sacrificial victim, and therefore had to be treated with respect. But its real significance was to point forward to the blood of the Lamb of God (Jesus Christ), who obtained 'eternal redemption' for his people (Hebrews 9:12) through shedding his own blood on the cross.

It is tragic that the Watchtower Society's policy denies Jehovah's Witnesses life-saving transfusions. But there is a greater tragedy. Failing to understand the deeper meaning of Old Testament blood laws may mean they also fail to find personal salvation in Christ.

LINKS

Material is drawn from both *Triple Helix*, 2001 (Sanderson). www.cmf.org.uk/literature/content.asp?context=article&id=1013 and *Nucleus*, 1993 (Fry). www.cmf.org.uk/literature/content.asp?context=article&id=461

testimony

Sarah says... Jehovah's Witnesses are encouraged to decline the use of blood products, even when critically ill, as they believe the Bible indicates that blood is sacred. During my surgery job, this issue arose with two patients.

The first was an elderly lady undergoing a leg amputation; she declined any blood, but thankfully made a good recovery. The second, a child undergoing a minor operation, was slightly more complex: the parents refused to consent to the use of blood products, and although a transfusion was unlikely to be needed, the surgical team were not happy to proceed. The hospital lawyers got a court decision, allowing the anaesthetist to give blood if required, despite the parents' wishes.

The two cases left me with mixed emotions, but above all a sense of frustration that these families were potentially declining a relatively simple, life-saving treatment, on the basis of Bible verses I interpret very differently. Reflecting on it later though, I was struck by their adherence to their faith, even in the face of crisis. Could I hold on to my principles in a similar situation?

Jehovah's Witnesses believe that blood transfusions are forbidden!

Galatians 3:25 **Now that faith has come, we are no longer under the supervision of the law.**

think it over...

1 What would be your first reaction on clerking in a patient who said they were a Jehovah's Witness?

2 How do you feel about your legal obligation not to give blood should a patient competently decline it?

3 If a Jehovah's Witness asked you about what the Bible says about blood, how might you respond?

TAKE HOME MESSAGE: **The Bible does not teach that we should abstain from blood transfusion**

Who is on the Lord's side? Who will serve the King?
Who will be his helpers, other lives to bring??
Frances R Havergal

Mission

Why should we go?

Jesus sends us to go into the entire world, whether on our doorstep or in far-flung areas, to preach the gospel to all creation and to demonstrate his compassion in practical ways; in healing the sick, binding up the broken-hearted and visiting those who are in prison. He will go with us and be with us always, as he has faithfully promised. As we serve God in all these needy places, opportunities will arise to talk of him and our motives for service.

How do I know what to do?

The needs are so great and it's all a bit bewildering; how do we find out where God is calling us? We must get to know God better to find out; he has a plan for each of us, he has prepared our service. We must be open to God's voice as we read the Bible, pray and talk with our friends and church communities. We must guard our call closely as it is easily trodden underfoot in the hectic pace of modern living and in the competition of the career ladder.

How long should I go for?

You can go for anything from one week to 50 years. Medics used to go abroad for a long time and stay for years. Some situations still need this kind of service, but now the emphasis is more on empowering and training local people. Sometimes visiting consultants and capacity builders can accomplish ten years of work in just a few weeks if skilled, focused and called by God.

When should I go?

If God has called you, you should go as soon as possible after you have the skills needed for what you're sent to do. This may mean sacrificing your normal career structure... but God is in charge of your career!

The basic medical skills of GPs who have completed their vocational training are enough for many front-line situations, sometimes with additional obstetrics thrown in. A diploma in Tropical Medicine sometimes helps but is not always needed. For centres of excellence you may need to wait till you're a specialist registrar or consultant. A year in biblical and cross-cultural training is helpful for the long-termer. But only delay for the shortest time necessary, as good resolutions and the cries of the impoverished are easily drowned by the lures of consultant posts or the security of general practice.

As medical people we have two passports: our national one and our medical registration

What is stopping you?

Do you have a call to remain right here where you are? If there is no pressing need for you here, there is a crying need for the gospel and for medical skills elsewhere. God has given you the medical knowledge to use in his service – he himself has prepared the good works for you to do. Everything is possible for him who believes, since with God, nothing is impossible and his word will accomplish his desire and achieve the purpose for which he sent it. With such great assurances from one such as God, and such a task to do, we must all be missionaries, at home or abroad.

Ted Lankester wrote as Director of InterHealth and **Rosie Knowles (née Beale-Preston)** as a medical student

LINKS   *Nucleus, July 2000. www.cmf.org.uk/publications/content.asp?context=article&id=289*

31

Let all the world in every corner sing, my God and King!
George Herbert

testimony

Vicky writes... I read 1 John 3:17 when I was at school and knew I had to do something to serve the poor – it was why I went into medicine. I was keen to get started so I set off for a rural mission hospital in Zambia, two years after I qualified and three weeks after getting married to an orthopaedic surgeon. We went for a year to see if we were cut out for longer term work and loved it, though there was a very steep learning curve.

I remember my very first night on call being summoned to deliver a footling breech! Thankfully the baby lived – though many other children I looked after on the paediatric ward didn't, and I found that very hard. But by the end of our time we knew that we wanted to return to the developing world so after I finished GP training we went to Malawi and ended up staying for ten years.

I got involved in lots of different things – paediatrics at the government hospital, more paediatrics at home (we went out with one baby and came back with three boys), starting a CMF and watching it grow, setting up a palliative care service – a brand new thing for Malawi – and my husband made lots of disabled children walk for the first time in their lives. There were many ups and downs – frustrations and disappointments, successes and failures, joys and sorrows. Best of all, there was lots of fun and a sense that we were doing Jesus' work where he wanted us to be.

You can go on mission from one week to 50 years

Matthew 28:19 Therefore go and make disciples of all nations, baptising them in the name of the Father and of the Son and of the Holy Spirit.

TAKE HOME MESSAGE: **Plan to go, be prepared to stay if called**

think it over...

1 What skills do you already have that could be used in the developing world? Think creatively!

2 If 'at home', what keeps you there currently? Do you feel called to be there?

3 How might you support those who are already overseas?

4 Have you considered a short-term trip (see Act 4)? When might you be able to go?

High cost treatments represent only a small part of NHS care, but they raise particular difficulties.
Helen Barratt

Resource allocation

Every working day, healthcare providers are confronted with the reality of limited resources. They are forced to make decisions and do the best they can within these constraints. Not only do they need to keep to a financial budget, they also have to allocate time and energy. This process is complicated by the task of balancing the needs of individual patients while at the same time considering the demands of the community as a whole.

Examining allocation decisions is important, and Christian thinking can enable the process. The Bible shows how God is concerned about the spiritual and physical health and wellbeing of populations, as well as being intimately concerned with the needs of individuals.

Considering individuals

Demands and desires – British culture has seen a move from paternalism, in which the doctor simply told the patient what to do, towards a situation where people increasingly question a doctor's decision. This consumerist attitude can place more demands on doctors, who have to assess whether it is appropriate to meet a particular demand or desire.

Biblically there is a call for people to use resources wisely. In the book of Genesis, human beings are called to be stewards of the world's resources. Applied to healthcare, this could imply that treatment only be given when it is genuinely needed. It is an incorrect use of resources to give inappropriate or unnecessary treatment just because a patient is asking for it.

Katie Wasson
wrote as a
clinical ethicist

Needs – Along with demands and desires, doctors are bombarded with a plethora of patients' needs. The first stage, however, is to define what is meant by a need, and who makes the decision that this is indeed a need. Is it the doctor or other professional, the patient, relatives, or even a judge?

It can be argued that basic needs should be met first, as they are the most pressing and urgent. It is often difficult to distinguish what patients need from what they want. Is, for example, breast enhancement a need or a want? What about removing a large visible tattoo, where a previous decision is radically affecting an individual's ongoing life?

Furthermore, patients may need treatments they do not want, such as chemotherapy, and want treatments they do not necessarily need, such as cosmetic surgery.

Rights and duties – We still need to determine the moral basis for meeting a person's needs. Sometimes this is expressed in the notion of rights and duties, and patients frequently demand their 'rights' in healthcare. Providers need to work out whether the person genuinely does have that right, and whether it is their duty to provide it.

For some patients, rights may conflict. A 'Do Not Resuscitate' order could be seen as a person exercising their right to avoid degrading treatment, but is denying their own right to life.

In addition, rights have corresponding duties and responsibilities. If a patient has a 'right' to healthcare, then some member of the healthcare team must have a duty to provide it. In the UK this means that individuals are entitled to use NHS services, including good quality care and appropriate treatment, but they are not necessarily entitled to have any and every treatment that they may request or demand.

Considerations of justice – Justice seen in terms of fairness requires that a universal and uniform standard of treatment is given to all people. It means that treatment should be consistent between individuals and all people in the same circumstances should be treated in the same way.

LINKS *CMF Files, 2002. www.cmf.org.uk/literature/content.asp?context=article&id=159*

The 'first law of health economics' states that 'the cheapest patient is a dead patient'.
John Wyatt

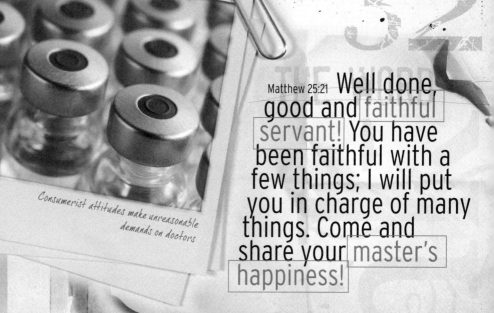

Consumerist attitudes make unreasonable demands on doctors

Matthew 25:21 **Well done, good and faithful servant! You have been faithful with a few things; I will put you in charge of many things. Come and share your master's happiness!**

Equality, like fairness, highlights a minimum standard below which the treatment of each patient should not fall. Equality requires that similar cases are treated in similar ways. As such, equality aims to avoid discrimination based on inappropriate grounds.

Both equality and fairness lead to consistency. They are helpful, but in health considerations they appear to mask over an important issue. Just as people are individuals, their health needs will be highly specific. It is very difficult to identify a pool of people so similar that they can instantly receive the same treatment.

The concept of equity recognises that different people need different treatment. Equity allows differences to occur, but only for morally justified reasons such as specific clinical needs. Giving people equal consideration is not the same as giving them identical treatment.

More than we deserve – Historically Christians have been at the forefront of establishing hospitals and providing healthcare, not because the patients deserve the care, but because the Christian shares Jesus' concern for weak and vulnerable members of society.

In the Gospels, we have clear accounts of how Jesus treated people as individuals. He saw and responded to many needs, because he had compassion on those who were suffering in body, mind and spirit. He healed the people who were brought to him, irrespective of the underlying cause of the illness. He acted from a principle of undeserved love, although did not heal everyone in the region.

It is easy to view resource allocation as a process of basic accounting, but Christians should expect that when they serve God great things happen. None of this, of course, detracts from the responsibility of being good stewards with the resources we have.

think it over...

1 What things can you do to use resources well? Think about:
a) Blood test requests (how many boxes do you tick?)
b) Prescribing (generic drugs)
c) Keeping admissions short where appropriate

2 This topic focuses on the UK's NHS. Are the principles different in a health system where patients pay directly for their care? What about private referrals in the UK?

3 Can 'patient choice' be squared with rational use of resources?

4 Think wider – should we always argue for more resources, or is there a limit to what it is desirable to spend?

95

THINK 33 *think... about...*

homosexuality

The past two decades have seen a growing acceptance of homosexuality and same-sex relationships as part of the 'normal range' of patterns of behaviour within our society.

Even asking whether there are underlying causes of homosexuality risks arousing criticism as the very question is politically incorrect. The result, as one psychiatrist put it, is that 'This is an area, par excellence, where scientific objectivity has little chance of survival'.

The problem was clearly displayed in a 2002 review of the current state of biomedical research on homosexuality. This concluded that so far the causes of homosexuality are unknown, that sexual orientation is likely to be influenced by both biological and social features and that the area could be studied. The review then argued that research into the causes of homosexuality would be unethical and should not occur. There is very little that is new published on the matter now and so most quoted research is quite dated.

While genes clearly have some bearing on behaviour, in the case of homosexuality, the evidence suggests that the genetic influence is only one factor. There was considerable media interest in 1993, when scientists claimed that variation in a region on the X chromosome (Xq28) was linked to male homosexual orientation. This study has since met with criticism and few people now give much weight to its evidence.

Twin studies are another way of looking for genetic influences. The most powerful studies look at identical twins who have been separated at birth. A 1986 study of four female and two male pairs concluded that genetic factors were hard to deny, but the number of subjects was too small to draw any meaningful conclusions. Also many identical twins have differing sexual orientations.

There is evidence that the culture in which a person

Peter Saunders wrote as CMF General Secretary

grows can influence their behaviour. At one extreme, in some cultures homosexuality is so uncommon that the language has no word to describe it. A study of nearly 35,000 adolescents showed that sexual orientation is not fixed at an early age. In fact, about a quarter of the 12-year-olds were unsure of their orientation. This steadily declined to about 5% of 18-year-olds. The authors noted that the observed relationship between sexuality and religiosity, ethnicity, and socioeconomic status provided further evidence of social influences on perceived sexual identity.

It is unwise and dishonest to ignore the fact that people living homosexual lifestyles are at greater risks of various forms of injuries than other members of the public. This is especially the case for homosexual men.

The most common high-risk sexual behaviours include oral-genital contact, mutual masturbation of the penis and anus and anal intercourse. While the vagina and the muscles within a woman's pelvis are well designed for sexual intercourse, this is not the case for the anatomy of the anus and rectum. Anal sex can lead to ulcers, inflammation, tearing of the muscles around the anus, and disruption in the rectum. This can cause incontinence and increase the risk of getting an infection.

Over the last few decades the Lesbian and Gay Christian Movement has argued that it is entirely compatible with the Christian faith not only to love a person of the same sex but also to express that love sexually. Most Christians, however, believe that the supreme authority in all matters of faith and conduct must be God's word. The LGCM view of homosexuality actually goes against the teaching of the Bible.

Throughout Scripture, sexual intercourse is seen as a gift from God to be enjoyed, but only in the context of a lifelong heterosexual marriage relationship. Jesus explains that not only is sexual intercourse outside marriage wrong, but even impure thoughts are sinful. Old Testament

LINKS *CMF File*, 2003. www.cmf.org.uk/literature/content.asp?context=article&id=154
Scientific references are omitted on this page for space and style reasons. Full referencing can be found in the online version.

Avoid hypocrisy

prohibitions against adultery and premarital sex are upheld in the New Testament, and homosexual behaviour is specifically ruled out on three occasions.

Christians who recognise that they have a homosexual orientation are more susceptible to temptation in this area than are others. This cannot however be used as an excuse for homosexual acts, which the Bible says are wrong. There is a difference between temptation and sin. The way of escape is to recognise that Jesus, who was 'tempted in every way just as we are', lives in us by his Spirit (Hebrews 4:15).

Christians who have a heterosexual orientation need to be patient and understanding towards Christians who don't. While urging them to refrain from homosexual acts they need also to be forgiving. They must also watch themselves, knowing that God views any sexual sin (heterosexual or homosexual) as equally wrong.

Christians must not victimise or abuse non-Christians who are practising homosexuals, but instead seek to understand them and treat them with love and respect, while not affirming their lifestyle choices.

To the gay rights lobby, when Christians of homosexual orientation resist the temptation to take part in homosexual acts, they are 'living a lie'. But from a biblical perspective they are exhibiting spiritual self-control.

There is no better model for a Christian response than when Jesus forgave a woman caught in adultery, but told her not to sin again. As Christians we must avoid hypocrisy and recognise that all people face sexual temptations. Indeed, most people sin sexually, at least in their minds if not in action, so we must not judge or condemn. Christians should explain the biblical position, warn of the dangers of a homosexual lifestyle, and offer support and encouragement to change.

Our efforts may be rejected, but this does not lessen our duty to help.

ed's thoughts...

The true incidence of homosexuality is much lower than generally believed. The commonly quoted figure of 10% comes from the 1948 Kinsey Report. This was based on a poorly designed study of a non-randomly selected group, 25% of whom were (or had been) prison inmates. Research published in 2001 indicated that 2.6% of both men and women reported homosexual partnerships.

Despite the popular media image of homosexual monogamy, several large studies reveal that less than 10% of homosexual men or women have ever experienced an exclusively monogamous relationship of greater than ten years duration. In one large early study, 74% of male homosexuals reported having more than one hundred partners in a lifetime, and 28% more than 1,000; 75% reported that over half of their partners were strangers. The figures for female homosexuals are substantially lower, but still significantly higher than those for married heterosexuals.

think it over...

1 Many with homosexual orientations have a very negative perception of Christians. Why might this be? What can you do to help change this?

2 Are you able to talk freely to anyone about sexual sin in your own life?

3 If homosexual orientation were conclusively proven to be genetically determined, how would that affect your views on this issue?

97

Truth

Truth matters. Our thinking and behaviour ought to depend on whether we believe something to be true or not.

'What is truth?' becomes a very important question.

The Bible raises the question explicitly in the context of John's account of Pilate's trial of Jesus:

Jesus said 'My kingdom is not of this world. If it were, my servants would fight to prevent my arrest by the Jews. But now my kingdom is from another place.' 'You are a king, then!' said Pilate. Jesus answered, 'You are right in saying I am a king. in fact, for this reason I was born, and for this I came into the world, to testify to the truth. Everyone on the side of truth listens to me.' 'What is truth?' Pilate asked. With this he went out again to the Jews and said, 'I find no basis for a charge against him'.

(John 18:36-38)

This exciting excerpt from the lengthy account of the several trials Jesus underwent (all to a greater or lesser extent a mockery of justice) indicates the central place of truth. Jesus' reason for coming into the world was 'to testify to the truth'. This challenges Pilate. In fact it may even overwhelm him because he then comes out with 'What is truth?' in an almost cynically dismissive way. We know from another Gospel that he literally 'washes his hands of the matter'.

Does Pilate's rhetorical question indicate that he was a Roman relativist? Was he someone who for cultural reasons could not accept that there could be such a thing as absolute truth? Briefly, relativism says 'Everything is relative'. You may recognise its ugly head when you have shared the Gospel with someone and they respond 'Oh well, that may be true for you, but it isn't true for me'. This laughable absurdity

Andrew Fergusson
wrote as General
Secretary of CMF

comes all too easily from the lips of the most intelligent and best educated of people, and it presents a devastating difficulty in dialogue.

Think about it a moment. Think about the statement 'everything is relative'. Is it a relative statement? If so, it is only relatively true, and so there must be some things which aren't relative, and so there must be some absolutes... Or is it rather an absolute statement? If so, the very existence of one absolute statement means that not everything is relative! Do you see how absurd it is? Yet I have had this said seriously to me by medical students in public debate!

Relativism cannot be true. It is a lie, but one that is both laughably obvious and subtly all-pervasive at the same time

If I present the Gospel and proclaim the whole of John 14:6 – 'Jesus answered, "I am the way and the truth and the life. No-one comes to the Father except through me"' – then many people say to me how arrogant I am. I point out that actually it is not me who first said it, but Jesus, who claimed to be the Son of God; but yes, they are very perceptive, that statement is either very arrogant or it's mad or it's true.

I then ask how they would decide who gets into Heaven? After a few gentle steps it becomes clear that, in fact, they themselves set up the standard. They themselves are the arbiters of justice. They themselves have that supreme spiritual authority! Is that not arrogant?

The truth is vital. I see the balance of evidence as clearly favouring not the devil's lies, but Jesus Christ who said: 'I am... the truth'.

LINKS Nucleus, 1992. www.cmf.org.uk/literature/content.asp?context=article&id=399

Our era is one of theological and moral confusion...
the apostle [Paul] summons us...
to be strong, brave and steadfast
John Stott

The one source of truth and knowledge

John 8:32 **Then you will know the truth, and the truth will set you free.**

testimony

Adele says... I was on a night shift in A&E and some standard sex jokes were being thrown around. A friend of mine was on the same shift and asked what I thought. This led on to more questions about sex, and I felt it was important to stand up for what I believe is 'absolute truth' – God's word revealed through the Bible – although I was keenly aware of my friend's opposing view point on several issues. She replied that she disagreed with what I said but was surprised as she had always imagined she would be really angry on hearing an opinion like mine. However as she knew me, and knew how much I really loved every person, regardless of any and every aspect of their behaviour, she could start to consider my point of view. It highlighted two really important points for me, that speaking the truth isn't always met by the negative reaction we (well I!) might imagine, but more importantly that our character and behaviour can often 'earn' us the right to have these conversations.

TAKE HOME MESSAGE: **Truth is defined by God, not by us**

think it over...

1 What examples can you think of to convince the relativist that there is such a thing as absolute truth? (eg. The earth cannot be both flat and round)

2 Are you convinced that the Bible is the source of absolute truth? If not, what do you need to convince you?

3 What areas of Christian teaching cause particular offence if presented as absolute truth?

Create communities of love which draw even more people to faith, and which validate the claims Christians make, by the lives Christians live.
Graham Cray

Speaking Out

Francis of Assisi said, 'I share my faith with everyone I meet and occasionally I use words'. There is a great truth here – actions of love and compassion do speak louder than mere speech about the love of Christ. But it disturbs me to hear Christians using this quotation as an excuse for keeping silent about the gospel and Christian values. I suspect that their real motivation may be cowardice.

Counting the cost

It is costly to live a life of obedience and service. It is costly to go on loving against the odds. It is costly to persevere when we are tempted to give up. And it is costly to give generously of our energy, time and money. But speaking for Christ and Christian values involves a different kind of cost – it makes us a target for attack.

Actions speak as loudly as words

Christians are often reluctant to risk ridicule, attack or 'loss of influence' by putting their heads above the parapet. Karl Marx was particularly disdainful of Christian priorities: 'You Christians have a vested interest in unjust structures which produce victims to whom then you can pour out your hearts in charity'. Whilst we would not embrace his communist philosophy and solutions, he did have a point. Real concern for the marginalised is evidenced both by charity and by speaking out.

Bishop Dom Helder Camara of Recife, Brazil, lived as a bishop among the poorest of the poor during the post 1964 Brazilian dictatorship. Camara challenged the obscene wealth of the rich and the embarrassing linkage of the Church with the powerful in his country. He observed: 'When I served the poor they called me a saint, when I asked why they were poor, they called

Peter Saunders wrote as CMF General Secretary

me a communist'. The prophets and apostles were persecuted for what they said, rather than what they did. John the Baptist did not shrink from confronting individuals in power – and he lost his head for it. And Jesus himself was crucified for his words, rather than his healing and miracles.

> The prophets and apostles were persecuted for what they said, rather than what they did

Our response for the voiceless

As Christian doctors we have a responsibility to speak out on behalf of those who have no voice: the poor, elderly or confused; those with head injuries, dementia or strokes; those suffering from chronic or psychiatric illness; the terminally ill; children, unborn children and human embryos. We need to speak out in everyday conversation, through our hospitals and medical associations, through government and on the Christian, secular and medical media – both nationally and internationally. And we need to encourage one another to make and create opportunities and remember that we are not alone.

Mordecai's words to Esther urging her to speak out when her own people were under threat are just as relevant to us today: 'If you remain silent at this time, relief and deliverance... will arise from another place, but you and your father's family will perish. And who knows but that you have come to royal position for such a time as this?' (Esther 4:14)

LINKS CMF News, 2005. www.cmf.org.uk/literature/content.asp?context=article&id=1577

To sin by silence when they should protest makes cowards of men.
Abraham Lincoln

Some things are worth shouting about

Proverbs 31:8-9 Speak up for those who cannot speak for themselves, for the rights of all who are destitute. Speak up and judge fairly; defend the rights of the poor and needy.

testimony

Richard says... I decided to get involved in opposing euthanasia. I have been writing quite a few letters in to newspapers and the medical press. Interestingly, I've had a lot of support emerging from some surprising quarters. Yes I have been criticised, and that can hurt, but slowly I'm developing a rather thicker epidermis!

Laurence says... speaking out in any context can bring criticism – whether it is publicly in the media, from peers at the BMA, or privately at work. Even in my days on the BMA student committee, Christian viewpoints were not always welcome. The first article I wrote for the BMA provoked an angry response from the then chairman of the ethics committee – amazed, I think, that anyone might challenge his position. Yet others on the committee were supportive, even though most didn't agree with my views. There was good opportunity for debate, which naturally led to conversations about the Christian convictions that led me to speak out.

TAKE HOME MESSAGE: **Esther was just an ordinary girl**

think it over...

1 Am I afraid of standing up for the gospel or for Christian values?

2 Is there a burning issue I feel burdened to speak out about?

3 How might we answer believers who say 'just stick to the gospel'?

4 How can we deal with our feelings when we face opposition and criticism?

BMA: be more active!

I wonder what you think of when you hear the words 'British Medical Association'? What springs to mind? The BMA's most important functions are as a voluntary professional association of doctors and an independent trade union. It is recognised as the voice of doctors and medical students in the UK. Whenever a medical issue is debated by government or the media, the BMA is often the first point of contact for agencies from *The Sun* to BBC News.

An article entitled, 'Do what only you can do' made me think about what I could do to influence my profession. Christian doctors lead hectic lives. We should question whether each cause or job we have been asked to undertake requires our unique gifting as a doctor, or generic skills that many non-medical colleagues will also have. 'Do what only you can do...'

There are many worthy uses of our time, but few roles require the specific attention of doctors. The BMA is a good example of this – only we can become members of the BMA, and make up the national 'voice of doctors'. On issues of morality or ethics, the BMA is usually asked for its opinion. A small number of doctors and students may influence a major change in the law of this country.

How to get involved

Join – An essential first step – if you haven't already! This can be done using the website *www.bma.org.uk*

Anna Soar wrote as a medical student

Attend local meetings – For members, the BMA website lists meetings of local divisions and regional councils. There are sometimes specific meetings for juniors in a given hospital, or deanery. Many are not well attended, meaning that you have a surprising amount of influence.

Attend the Junior Doctors' Conference and write motions – Each year there is a conference for junior doctors. There isn't necessarily a lot of discussion about abortion and euthanasia, but a lot of time is often spent on employment or training issues - which may be just as important in our Christian walk as obvious questions of ethics.

As well as a chance to make your views heard, this conference is a good place to meet others who are active in the BMA. You may be the first Christian some of them have had a conversation with!

How many of us get our glossy *BMJ*s each week, have a quick flick through and then bin them?

Stand for election to a BMA committee – If you want to do more, there is a national Junior Doctors' Committee to which you can be elected. There are committees for trainees in some specialties, and there is no reason why junior doctors should not hold local divisional BMA offices. This will allow you much more chance to bring influence to bear – both on the chairs of such committees, and on the agenda that they follow. It is at this point that you can raise the profile of issues like justice and ethics.

Go to the Annual Representative Meeting (ARM) – The ARM is the national annual meeting for everyone in the BMA. The ARM agenda is made up of motions passed at the conferences of the different branches of the BMA. By getting a seat at the ARM you are able to vote on the submitted motions and the ones that pass become the policy of the whole BMA. You are personally able to influence national BMA policy and therefore what the 'voice of UK doctors' says!

LINKS Nucleus, 2007. www.cmf.org.uk/literature/content.asp?context=article&id=1969

Of all things, guard against neglecting God in the secret place of prayer.
William Wilberforce

Join: an essential first step

Proverbs 24:11 Rescue those being led away to death; hold back those staggering toward slaughter.

Any BMA member can apply through their local division for a seat at this meeting; it is an amazing opportunity to see how the BMA operates, and to find out about the current hot topics. The BMA website explains how to go about seeking a place. A number of CMF members have attended and spoken at these meetings over the past few years. There is a specific debate on ethics during the meeting, and issues such as assisted suicide and embryo research are often discussed.

Pray – Please pray for the leaders of our profession and our country – 'I urge, then, first of all, that requests, prayers, intercession and thanksgiving be made for everyone – for kings and all those in authority, that we may live peaceful and quiet lives in all godliness and holiness.' (1 Timothy 2:1-2)

Be a 'Wilberforce' – 200 years after the Christian MP William Wilberforce tirelessly campaigned for the abolition of slavery, we are in no less need of Christians in places of influence who will stand for truth. What greater confidence can we have than to know that Christ is with us 'always, to the very end of the age'?

I find myself wanting to say, especially to young people: 'Don't be content with the mediocre! Don't settle for anything less than your God-given potential! Be ambitious and adventurous for God! God has made you a unique person by your genetic endowment, upbringing and education. He has Himself created you and gifted you, and He does not want His work to be wasted. He means you to be fulfilled, not frustrated. His purpose is that everything you have and are should be stretched in His service and in the service of others '...only then can we hope to hear from Christ those most coveted of all words, 'Well done, good and faithful servant!' (John Stott in *Issues Facing Christians Today*)

think it over...

1 Someone in your church tells you over coffee 'Doctors should be on the wards, not arguing at conferences'. How would you explain the importance of things like the BMA to her?

2 What could you do to promote Christian principles in the BMA, or your Royal College?

3 Some think that political work distracts from spreading the gospel. How would you answer them?

TAKE HOME MESSAGE: **You have more influence than you may think!**

Engage with SOCIETY

Freedom and liberty lose out by default because good people are not vigilant
Desmond Tutu

'Ah, Sovereign Lord', I said, 'I do not know how to speak; I am only a child' (Jeremiah 1:6). There must have been a mistake. This young, sensitive and introspective priest was surely destined for a quiet life, leading and nurturing the religious believers in Judah. Could he really be 'a prophet to the nations', 'to uproot and tear down, to destroy and overthrow, to build and to plant'?

In church, we often hear a call to be godly in all we do. Yet this is often limited to personal relationships with our family, friends and colleagues. Jeremiah was being called to serve God in public life, in the midst of society's raging debates. Christians today should do the same – but where do we begin?

Looking at God

Our God cares greatly about how societies function. As we draw close to him, we feel more acutely his concerns for justice and equality, and his love for the poor and needy. As we read the Bible and learn about God's concerns, we become more like him in hating evil and striving for what is right. God is characterised by his justice. We should strive for change wherever there is abuse of power – whether in healthcare rationing, international law, foreign policy or medical ethics.

Looking around us

As Christians who seek to emulate God's care for all people, we should not hide ourselves from the wrong things going on around us. Rather, we should investigate and expose them, demonstrating a better way to live – a rational and truthful way.

It's good for Christians to listen to the outcry that rises from our world. The Gross Domestic Product of the poorest 48 nations is less than the combined wealth of the world's three richest people. Less than one percent of what the world spends on weapons each year was needed to put every child into school by the year 2000; yet it didn't happen.

Looking at ourselves

The theme of faith working itself out in action is consistent throughout the book of James:

Suppose a brother or sister is without clothes and daily food. If one of you says to him, 'Go, I wish you well; keep warm and well fed,' but does nothing about his physical needs, what good is it? In the same way, faith by itself, if it is not accompanied by action, is dead. (James 2:15-17)

Christians have a unique calling to care for those in need, and the power of God to help them do so. We are a big part of God's response to poverty, suffering and injustice.

The great need of human beings is to know, love and worship their creator. The great commission, to make disciples of all nations, was given to all Christians. But another great command in Scripture is to shine before men – like a lamp on a stand or stars in the sky – to be the light of the world. We do this, wherever we are, by standing out as different.

The Old Testament prophets had a rough ride. They were sent to confront kings and priests about their failure to lead as God wanted. Jeremiah, a timid and sensitive soul, was such a prophet, who ended up being thrown into a cistern and left to rot until his friends rescued him. People do not like being told that they are doing wrong. But the great injustices in the world, be they poverty in Africa, abortion, racism, or genocide, do need to be exposed.

But the biblical message is not simply one of condemnation.

David Randall wrote as a medical student

Nucleus, 2007. www.cmf.org.uk/publications/content.asp?context=article&id=2013

testimony

Helen says... 'Doctor bashing' has almost become a sport for many people, but polls consistently confirm that medicine remains amongst the most highly respected professions. Our title also still holds some influence, and I confess I've used mine more than once in the hope of getting better customer service! Many people still trust a doctor, and although this power can be abused, it also presents us with great opportunities.

I have been surprised and humbled at times when people have sought my opinion as a Christian doctor, and this has presented opportunities to put forward a biblical perspective on everything from abortion to social justice. Sometimes this has led to uncomfortable conversations, such as when a friend asked my opinion about the in vitro fertilisation treatment he and his wife were going through, but it remains a privilege to be invited to give a biblical perspective.

A unique calling to care for those in need

Isaiah 6:8 Then I heard the voice of the Lord saying, "Whom shall I send? And who will go for us?" And I said, "Here am I. Send me!"

We do not simply condemn abortion; we must also show how women can cope with having children at awkward times and give them the necessary support. We don't simply attack unfettered capitalism; we show people how to set up a system that allows money to be made without trampling those at the bottom of the pile.

Listening out for God's call

Both Jeremiah and Isaiah protested, on the grounds of inexperience and inability, against their appointment as prophets. God gives us the words to say and the strength to say them; all that we bring is a willingness to be used.

Begin small. Heavy involvement in public policy is not for everyone. But it is for some – so get involved. Push at some doors, and see which ones open. The need is so great and the love of God is so compelling that we simply cannot sit still and leave the world to its own devices.

think it over...

1 Try reading about a particular issue that interests you and commit to pray regularly over it for a period of time

2 Think about what issues come up in day to day conversation at work and think about how you could tackle them in conversation

3 For the more actively minded, get involved in local BMA activities or represent fellow trainees on committees - good on your CV as well as good witness!

TAKE HOME MESSAGE: **God might use anyone - even you!**

The Great Commission is not an option to be considered; it is a command to be obeyed.
Hudson Taylor

Go over seas

We must go through many hardships to enter the kingdom of God. (Acts 14:22). The Apostle Paul knew all about hardships. He spoke these words soon after being stoned and left for dead. We are called to suffer hardships for the kingdom of God but we rarely do so.

The day after studying this passage I was at a medical charity discussing a missionary who was struggling as the only doctor running a Christian hospital in a Muslim area in Africa. Someone said, 'Surely people in CMF could go to help?'

The next day the *BMJ* arrived with two challenging articles. The first was by Professor Chris Lavy. He described how, having just become a consultant and started up private practice in orthopaedics, he gave it up to go to Malawi, a country with the same population as London but no orthopaedic surgeon. The second article, by another CMF member working in Afghanistan, described possible future problems in the NHS if he could not do a face-to-face appraisal. He therefore would not be able to work as a locum in the UK when on leave.

I was able to relate to these articles. Several years ago, I returned from running a mission hospital in Uganda. I did a GP returner scheme, for which there is now no funding locally. It was a useful reintroduction in a safe environment to UK life. Had I returned any later I would have had to sit exams. What can CMF members do?

Fill gaps

Nick Wooding
wrote as a GP, and former Superintendent of Kiwoko Hospital in Uganda

First, we can fill the gaps in other health systems. Statistics show the need for this. We might think we have staffing problems in the UK but we are still 150 times better off than Malawi. It would be easier health-wise for a younger person, rather than a retired doctor, to work near the Sahara. The experience would be invaluable. A surgeon does more operating in a mission hospital than on a training scheme.

Lobby

Secondly, we can lobby for change. Are there CMF members in high places in the medical establishment? I would hope so. Are they speaking up for those who work abroad or who would like to? I do not know. Are they pushing the Royal Colleges to recognise experience abroad? And recommending doctors gain it? Can we foresee a time when CVs will be rejected if candidates have not spent time in the developing world?

Use our leave

Thirdly, we can think about using our leave to do appraisals abroad, or to help a single-handed doctor get leave or administration time.

Give

Fourthly, if for career reasons we do not go, then instead we can always give financially. When it comes to suffering hardships for the kingdom of God, this may be the hardest. Are we willing to live simply so that others may simply live? How countercultural is our way of life among our affluent peers?

Could we have stepped in?

One day we will enter heaven and worship with every tribe, nation, colour and tongue. The people dying now because we neither went nor gave are in areas of the world where the majority would call themselves Christian. One day we will have to look them in the face. Could we have stepped into their suffering, relieving their hardships by increasing ours just a little?

LINKS   *Triple Helix*, 2007. www.cmf.org.uk/literature/content.asp?context=article&id=1997

Genie says... During my junior posts, I managed to get three separate leaves – a mixture of annual and study leave – for short term medical mission trips. I went to Tibet during my A&E post, India during psychiatry and Uganda during my obstetrics and gynaecology job.

On all three trips I focused mainly on community health and teaching rural health workers. They were all very different experiences in terms of what I did, but definitely worthwhile. Initially, I struggled to find projects suitable for trips of just two or three weeks, but it's amazing what's out there if you look hard enough. Once I got to know the right people, the offers started pouring in!

Fitting overseas trips into my long-term NHS job as a GP trainee has brought me much needed perspective on just how good English healthcare is! I have also got to know other Christian medics who are more mature in professional and spiritual terms. There are many fabulous people out there who thrive on doing God's work in the middle of nowhere!

Back home, I find that consultants and colleagues take a lot of interest in my trips. It's amazing what conversation comes out of telling people where you've been on holiday!

Sarah says... Given Jesus' call, it's strange that directing your life towards being a long-term missionary is actually unusual. It has been a lonely path. To try and keep the call alive over the years, I have learnt languages, worked abroad, studied Islam, prayed over Muslim countries, been on church mission council, visited missionaries and ministered with Muslims in the UK.

I could not understand why God wanted me to do higher specialist training, but as it turns out, the North African countries I am looking to go to would probably not take me otherwise. For me this has been an important confirmation that God has the call in hand. As I am now in higher specialist training the time to go seems within sight. Sometimes I think that my greatest fear is never getting married because of following this call. But actually my greatest fear is meeting Jesus and never having fulfilled the call that I know he has given me.

Doing God's work is often out of our comfort zone

From everyone who has been given much, much will be demanded; and from the one who has been entrusted with much, much more will be asked.

Luke 12:48

think it over...

1 Am I suffering any form of real hardship for the kingdom of God – whether at home or overseas?

2 Could I 'fill a gap'?

3 Could I lobby my royal college to recognise overseas training?

4 How could I use my leave creatively for going overseas?

5 Should I be giving more to support medical missionaries?

> *True influence is about more than just someone listening. It's about action.*
> *And it's about change. If I simply buy your book and read a few chapters,*
> *but don't put anything into action, are you really influencing me?*
> *Brad Lomenick*

Influence the next generation

Our young people are suffering from the consequences of sex outside marriage and the disintegration of home life. We believe that safe(r) sex teaching has contributed to this by promoting sex at a younger age and outside a moral framework. Our desire is to see this ungodly teaching replaced by one from a Christian perspective in order to help rebuild the family in our society.

With this in mind, in 2002 we formed a charity called Lovewise, together with a local secondary school head teacher. (See *lovewise.org.uk* for further details). Its aim is to encourage young people to consider the blessings of marriage and the rightness and benefits of keeping sex for marriage. It sends presenters into schools and youth groups using Powerpoint, video interviews and personal testimonies. Our material is also available for individual class teachers and youth group leaders.

What does Lovewise teach?

Ideally intimate issues of sexuality should be modelled and taught by a child's parents. Sadly such teaching is often avoided or unhelpful. So what can we provide as a substitute?

Upholding God-given boundaries for sex

Many are raised in homes where there are few rules on how to conduct themselves in relationships. Many are pressurised to go further physically than they wish (especially girls). We talk about how media and peer-pressure contribute to this. Most younger pupils seem willing to accept that God made marriage and sex. Some are surprised to find Christians saying that sex is good; many find it harder to accept that God intends sex to be kept for marriage. Nevertheless, we sense a relief that there are boundaries

Chris Richards wrote as a consultant paediatrician in Newcastle

and some are pleased to hear that they are not being 'cold' or awkward if they long for and insist upon life-long commitment before giving themselves physically.

Encouraging pupils to aspire to marriage and parenthood

Few of them have received any clear guidance on what kind of family future they should look forward to. We use a clip of a wedding ceremony to explain the nature of marriage. Whilst we try to be sensitive to the varied family background of pupils, we do not want the mistakes of a previous generation to be foisted on the next. Interestingly, despite the poor press that marriage gets, the majority of our pupils still hope to marry at some stage. We explain the superior nature of marriage compared to living together in terms of duration, fidelity and childrens' upbringing. Rather than the safe(r) sex perspective of pregnancy avoidance, we explain the great privilege of sharing in the creation of new life and the joy of parenthood in marriage.

Considering the consequences of sex outside marriage

We show them a photo of a pregnant woman and a man with AIDS to remind them that choices they make in relationships can have life and death consequences. We explain how the condom has been made widely available, but has failed to afford the protection promised. They are surprised to hear studies show a wide range of protection for different infections (little or none for warts and herpes, 40% for chlamydia, 90% for HIV). We also tell them about the long term consequences of STIs.

Holding out God's offer of forgiveness and a fresh start

How hopeless it would be if we simply held up God's commands without

LINKS   *Nucleus, 2005. www.cmf.org.uk/publications/content.asp?context=article&id=1629*

testimony

Anika says... I was apprehensive standing in front of a Year Nine class for the first time, aware that I was about to share a foreign message. I would be talking about emotive subjects; the pain of broken relationships, the consequences of casual sex. I would be encouraging them to have a higher view of sex and not settle for the shiny, gift-wrapped product they are offered by today's culture.

I was a presenter with Lovewise during fourth and fifth year of medical school, teaching children about marriage, sex and relationships as God created them. I was amazed how hungry children are for this teaching. They ask questions, some insightful, some silly. They want answers from someone they can trust. After hearing presentations several children told me of their decision to wait longer before having sex and many others have been equipped to make more informed and hopefully wiser future choices.

Passing on wisdom

1 Corinthians 6:19 **Do you not know that your body is a temple of the Holy Spirit, who is in you, whom you have received from God? You are not your own.**

...his response to our disobedience. Though we haven't yet had any obvious response to our simple explanation of the Cross, we know that many need to hear of God's grace as they wrestle with guilt, pain and low self esteem from past mistakes. We encourage those who have made mistakes to ask God's forgiveness and make a new start.

Offering practical advice

We give them help on how to avoid sexual intimacy whilst going out. This includes the need for self-control, the dangers of alcohol and provocation through dress, behaviour and pornography.

We have very little idea of the effects of our presentations on the pupils, although occasional comments give us encouragement. Many teachers thank us for teaching what they know is true but fear to teach themselves in the current philosophical climate. We give the presentations in faith remembering the power of God's word and the Lord's reminder of the harvest from seed that we scatter, which grows night and day independent of us!

think it over...

1. What opportunities to shape the next generation do you have in day-to-day work?

2. How might you support the children in your church?

3. Do you feel confident yourself that the above messages about sex and relationships are correct?

TAKE HOME MESSAGE: **Pass on the teaching that has shaped your life to the next generation**

Lobby Politicians

The abolition of slavery, the suffragettes, the building of hospitals and the end of child labour were all inspired by Christians engaging in politics.

We should campaign on issues where we are likely to make a difference. We must keep up to date with news, both generally and within our profession. Worthwhile subjects include those where there are current court cases or consultations taking place – or those where there is an imminent debate scheduled in Parliament. The resources section contains links to a number of helpful websites that summarise such issues.

More weight may be attached to the views of doctors on medical and ethical issues than those of other Christians, so we should make use of this privileged position. We should not ignore non-medical issues, but be aware that other Christians may be better placed to campaign about them.

We may need to concentrate on more obviously 'Christian' areas (such as ethics) since few others will. This is not to say that issues such as doctors' training or student debt are unimportant, but since there are others already campaigning in these areas, our time is better used where workers are few.

Whom should we lobby?

Members of Parliament are strategic targets for lobbying. With frequent changes of law in medical ethics, MPs have a lot of power in this area. Parliament sets laws, and the law plays a powerful role in shaping opinion. The fact that abortion is legal in the UK legitimises it in some people's eyes and many doctors who would not perform euthanasia now might do so if the law was changed.

We have the most influence over our local MPs, as they need our votes to stay in office at forthcoming elections! Writing to the appropriate government minister may be effective in some circumstances, as may letters or emails to members of the House of Lords when a relevant issue is under debate there.

Laurence Crutchlow wrote as a medical student

Local councillors also have influence over things that may interest believers, such as policy on homelessness or licensing of sex shops. An increasing amount of law is determined at a European level, so Members of the European Parliament should not be forgotten.

We must make sure we do not miss the opportunities that we are given

How should we go about it?

We need to understand the issues. The CMF website is an invaluable resource on medical ethics. Although it is important to be accurate and well researched, we should not be put off lobbying by a lack of knowledge. Many politicians will have far less knowledge in medical ethics than we do – even if we are FY1 doctors! Even our limited understanding will be used by God for his glory.

Letters or emails are a key tool in lobbying. If writing to politicians on a medical issue, remember that they will have little or no medical knowledge, so clear simple explanations are needed. It is best to make a point specific to the vote or debate in question. State why you are interested in the issue, why you consider it important, state your viewpoint, and urge your MP to vote in the appropriate way.

Petitions are still influential – and can now be set up electronically on government websites. Nearly 1.8 million people signed a petition on road charging in 2007, leading to the apparent abandonment of the policy. New media, in particular political blogs, may also have influence, although some suggest that this is overstated.

And finally, we mustn't forget to pray. This is ultimately an area of spiritual battle, where the worldly odds are often against us.

LINKS *Nucleus, 2002. www.cmf.org.uk/literature/content.asp?context=article&id=24*

Expect great things from God; attempt great things for God.
William Carey

Raise your hand and be counted

Isaiah 10:1-2 **Woe to those who make unjust laws, to those who issue oppressive decrees, to deprive the poor of their rights and withhold justice from the oppressed of my people.**

testimony

Andrew says... I heard a talk on abortion by Peter Saunders where he stated that when legal abortion was being debated in the 1960s, Christians thought it would never happen and so were apathetic – and then it did! This jolted me into action and I was determined to make sure that Physician Assisted Suicide didn't become legal 'on my watch'.

Consequently I spoke at the BMA conference where this was debated and I got my friends to write in to their MPs and Lords about the issue. I used to think that policy was determined by the majority but it is not at all – the most vocal minority often get their way! This gave me great encouragement that my small efforts could make a difference – and so far euthanasia is still illegal. I encourage you to get involved in medical and national politics because you can make a difference.

TAKE HOME MESSAGE: **We cannot stay silent in the face of wrong laws**

think it over...

1 What have you seen or heard in the news today? What issues concern you?

2 Are there any current issues in the news that a Christian doctor might have particular views on?

3 Who is your MP? Your MEP? Your local councillor?

4 What current issue might you be able to write to your MP about?

Mission at home

Living among the disadvantaged — a story. **An architecture graduate and his wife, Crawford and Sheila, were inspired by the concept of 'incarnational ministry' mentioned in Philippians 2:5-7, where 'Jesus... made himself nothing, taking the very nature of a servant'.** So they went to live among those with whom they wanted to share their faith. After finishing college they moved to a relatively deprived area in Glasgow, where they brought up their two children. They faced opposition from some Christian friends and family who questioned what they were trying to do, sending their children to a primary school described as 'an annexe to the local prison'. Crawford rented a shop in the area for use as an office – not the best place for business. However, people who would not set foot in a church were willing to come into the office and chat. There was in fact a good Christian influence in the primary school.

They moved on a few years later to a housing estate in Dundee at the invitation of the local church. Living in a housing association flat, they could experience the reality of the area 24 hours a day, and there were opportunities to visit schools, build relationships and get involved in the community. A building project at the church led them to request help from local men who were unemployed, leading to the realisation that for many the main issue was not lack of money or lack of opportunities, but rather a lack of self-worth.

Becky MacFarlane
wrote as a GP in Glasgow

What about me?

As doctors there are many opportunities to work in a voluntary capacity with the vulnerable. Some live in more deprived areas or become involved in a local church in such an area, building relationships and doing what they can, for example with the children in Sunday school or at a holiday club. Others are leaders at camps for underprivileged children or children in care. The Salvation Army, local City Mission or other groups such as Oasis may provide means for helping the homeless. There are schemes for supporting the housebound, for example helping patients discharged from hospital settle back into their home. ACET (AIDS Care Education and Training) and other groups provide similar support for those with AIDS. There are opportunities to teach literacy skills to native speakers, or support those learning English as a second language.

Doctors may choose to work with the homeless, asylum seekers, disabled or patients in nursing homes. Those in hospital jobs and students on placement can be distinctive in the way they treat a patient with dementia or the terminally ill, the alcoholic or the teenager admitted following an overdose.

We are called to imitate God in caring for the weak and vulnerable

Three years ago I saw a post advertised for a salaried general practitioner (GP) to work in a practice in inner city Glasgow that expected to be taking on 500 asylum seekers. I had previously felt I lacked experience for such a post but I soon realised that dealing with such patients would be a challenge for any doctor. I have found great satisfaction in the job whilst also finding that the sorrows and frustrations experienced by my patients have had a profound effect on me.

Health needs of asylum seekers

Medical issues are broad and include access to healthcare as well as a

Nucleus, 2003. www.cmf.org.uk/literature/content.asp?context=article&id=394

testimony

Elizabeth says... As a student I lived in a deprived community in Manchester as part of the Eden project; involved in outreach and youth work. It was amazing to see how open people were, unlike my nice but often cynical doctor mates; the people where I lived knew they weren't perfect. They knew they were broken and needed God. We saw families open their homes and welcome us in to hear what God had to say to them. We saw genuine and lasting change in people's lives. It was so humbling. Life is nice as a doctor. We have money and instant respect. We're at the top of the pile. Not like the 'chavs', the unemployed and the single mums, the drug addict and the yob hanging about on the street corner. They are all hated by our society.

The thing that struck me about Jesus is that he always noticed the person who others ignored. He had time for the people others didn't; he was willing to touch the untouchable. He looks at the world upside down. I have felt more and more called to live like him and take time for these people.

I have come to know a God who has a soft spot for rebels.
Philip Yancey

Leviticus 19:33 **When an alien lives with you in your land, do not mistreat him.**

variety of medical conditions. In some parts of the UK it may be difficult to register with a GP. Language barriers require good interpreters and an efficient system for obtaining their services when needed. Most medical problems are similar to those faced by British patients, from upper respiratory tract infections and dyspepsia to asthma and diabetes, although there are higher incidences of some conditions in those from certain parts of the world. Many suffer from insomnia and are anxious or depressed. Pregnancy-related issues are also common, including unwanted pregnancy, miscarriage and stillbirth. Some struggle with impotence whilst others face infertility. Many are concerned about their children who may also have psychological problems because of their experiences. As Christians we are called to imitate God in caring for the weak and vulnerable. As we do this, we need his power and love, his wisdom and guidance. With his help we can make a difference in our own nation and around the world.

think it over...

1 Can you think of people in your church who have been 'missionaries at home'?

2 How do you deal with vulnerable patients? Is there anything you might need to change about this?

3 What opportunities to help the vulnerable do you have in your current job?

TAKE HOME MESSAGE: **There are lots of opportunities to make a difference as a Christian**

Study at Bible College

*A thorough knowledge of the Bible
is worth more than a college education.*
Theodore Roosevelt

Junior doctors embrace a life of physical and emotional pressure which others cannot appreciate. How many times have you heard Christian colleagues say that their early years were a time of working flat out, with devotional life and Christian health under severe pressure? Why not take time out?

A short course at a Bible college may be a heaven-sent opportunity to sleep (at night, not during lectures), pray, study the Bible, talk out problems with a sympathetic listener and reflect on where you might be heading.

Teaching at Belfast Bible College, I often notice that those who benefit most from our courses have seen something of the traumas of life. Reflecting on their experiences, they begin to think theologically about what they have been doing and develop fresh approaches to familiar problems.

- Time spent reading and writing about what you have already experienced offers an opportunity to develop a foundation for future actions which is both biblical and practical.
- You may take courses in counselling to help vulnerable patients, or in Christian mission to explore opportunities for service overseas.
- You will spend time studying the Bible for its own sake and applying your substantial intellect to the Scriptures in new and exciting ways.
- You will have space for quietness, prayer and meditation.
- You will discover a community of worship. A term at Bible college may inject new life and new approaches.

Drawbacks such as financial costs are not to be ignored, but saving beforehand, forgoing some luxuries during study, and a year or two paying off a small loan afterwards would

Drew Gibson wrote while teaching at Belfast Bible College

be far from impossible. College fees are by no means prohibitive.

Some medics may see a CV showing time at Bible college as a sign of low commitment, but presenting the time you have spent in terms of innovative and lateral thinking, risk taking, and self motivated study may help.

A short course at a Bible college may be a heaven-sent opportunity

Conclusions

A term in Bible college may trigger a radical re-orientation of your career. Unthinkable as it may seem to the upwardly mobile junior, rising to the top of the cardiothoracic surgery ladder may not be the ultimate goal in life after all. Perhaps God has other plans. If God calls us to step off the ladder, surely he is perfectly capable of providing for us if he calls us to step back on to the ladder again? He will either restore to us what we have set aside for a while or he will move us in a new direction by opening new opportunities. Time out might be just the way to rekindle your personal spiritual life and to start breathing life back into the healthcare system in the UK and beyond.

LINKS   *Triple Helix, 1998. www.cmf.org.uk/publications/content.asp?context=article&id=846*

testimony

Alex says... I had wanted to study theology and mission for a long time when a career break finally allowed me to step out of medicine for a year. And a year without a bleep – it was a no-brainer! So I signed up for All Nations Christian College, in rural Hertfordshire.

It was great to have time for self-directed learning, in a library without a single medical journal. We gorged ourselves on Bible commentaries, cross-cultural studies, church history, Jewish interpretation of the Old Testament, anthropology and much much more. It is worth saying that if you want rest and recuperation, Bible colleges are academic institutions, so you need to enjoy disciplined study and honest debate. But it needn't be a threat to your faith. In fact, it was very reassuring to read the worst assaults on biblical Christianity and realise that the foundations are very secure. You don't have to commit intellectual suicide to be a Christian; in fact we are just following the evidence where it leads. And thankfully, our course was very practical, training us in life skills for many settings, including car maintenance, hairdressing, communication skills, performing arts and ethnomusicology!

Overall though, it was fellow students, from over 20 countries, who had the biggest impact on me. It's surprising how easily our aspirations are shaped by those we spend the most time with. So it was refreshing and challenging to live with missionaries who were more concerned with the Gospel than financial security. It was also a shock to be sharing a room again, and to be on a toilet cleaning rota. But I suspect both were good for me!

In terms of funding, medics have an enormous advantage over virtually everyone else. Locums at weekends and holidays easily covered costs, which were extremely good value compared with any medical course. So do consider it, if you think it will equip you wherever you are called to.

Time out to rekindle your spiritual life

Psalm 1:2 **But his delight is in the law of the Lord, and on his law he meditates day and night.**

think it over...

1 How much 'formal' Bible study do you get time for?

2 Is time out for a Bible college course a possibility for you?

3 What might you need to do to be able to take time out?

4 If you can't take time out, have you thought of correspondence courses?

TAKE HOME MESSAGE: **Time out of medicine is well worth it**

117

Work with CMF

Reading the Gospels reminds us that Jesus spent a **disproportionate amount of time with a small number of people.** Yet his impact spread far beyond the twelve people with whom he spent so long.

Working for CMF is not dissimilar. True, there are opportunities to connect with large numbers at once – for example in giving a talk to big group, or publishing journals like *Nucleus* or *Triple Helix*, which reach thousands. But much of the work is done more quietly – over coffee with a student, or in an informal chat at the end of a seminar or talk.

Working this way is labour intensive. Of course many non-medics can and do play a vital role in helping medical students and doctors to grow in their faith – with church student workers and UCCF staff being highly valued. But there are some things that only a doctor can easily help with. Recent discussions I've had have involved the challenges of working in sexual health and family planning clinics, and the issues raised over contraception; what opportunities there might be for Christian witness for a doctor in secure environments; and whether one can or should discuss spiritual matters with patients, and how the General Medical Council would see this. Even more generic discussions, like career planning, or how to cope with a busy job when married, are often easier when between two medics.

This is where you come in. CMF's student ministry has a long history of support from part-time doctors, working both in medicine and for CMF. This has now extended to CMF's graduate ministry, and we hope it will grow further in future. But we need people if we are to give more input to individuals, in the way Jesus did.

A number of models are possible. Student staffworkers have usually worked two days each week for CMF in a paid post, alongside part-time medical training or general practice posts. Associate staffworkers would usually work a day or so a week on a voluntary basis. Interns spend a year doing more intensive work, usually with students, often in a break between foundation and specialist training jobs, on a voluntary basis, perhaps supported by locums or alongside Bible college study.

A single conversation can be life-changing

CMF is also actively encouraging doctors to consider whether they could drop a session or two a week of clinical work, to voluntarily support students and junior doctors in their area. For those with even just an hour a week to spare, it is sill possible to support local medical students.

The biggest obstacle has always been lack of people, not lack of funds. There are some practical issues, particularly for those who want to train part-time. But often the real obstacle is not having the vision and motivation for the work in the first place – since the practical difficulties can usually be sorted out.

If you think this might be for you, why not pray through it, and talk with a couple of trusted Christian friends? It isn't an easy option, and may not have the glamour of overseas mission, or 'full-time ministry'. The challenges of balancing medical life with a busy ministry will test you, but also bring growth.

If you decide to go for it, get in touch with the CMF office to talk it through, and plan ahead – since many practical obstacles are much easier to solve ahead of time. We look forward to welcoming more of you to the team!

Laurence Crutchlow wrote as part-time CMF Associate Head of Student Ministries and part-time GP

B ecky worked as a student staffworker from 2002-2005... Being a staffworker was great. I grew loads spiritually and it was wonderful to see God at work in people's lives. At times it could be frustrating – my CMF supervisors seemed so busy and sometimes I felt guilty about ringing them! But, having said that, they always listened to my queries and gave me good advice.

Looking back I wouldn't change anything really. I'm glad I did it. Certainly it's given me a more holistic attitude towards medicine, and my presentation skills are so much better! As well as that, working for CMF during my GP training gave me more opportunities to think through the practical application of ethical issues we face as Christian doctors.

My only slight regret is that my training was completed more slowly as I worked with CMF, meaning that I was less established in my career by the time I had children. On the other hand, working for CMF led to me meeting my husband Gareth, so I've a lot to thank the Fellowship for!

K erry was a field intern in 2010-2011... In the run up to applications for core training jobs I realised I didn't feel ready to pick a career path, and so began to explore my options for a year out. I contacted CMF, and after some discussion and prayer, found myself with the opportunity to be a part-time 'field intern' in my year out. I chose to fill the other part of my time with distance learning theology.

This year has provided me with opportunities and experiences I would never otherwise have had, such as teaching abroad and on day courses like *Confident Christianity*. It has been an incredible journey – with ups and downs, but what a privilege to spend a whole year immersed in the Bible, meeting up with students and travelling to conferences!

It is a challenge at times to balance work with study, and it can feel rather isolating, but I have been blessed to have some fantastic mentors who have been really supportive and from whom I have learnt much. Would I recommend being an intern for CMF? Of course! If God is steering you towards it, go for it – he will take care of the rest.

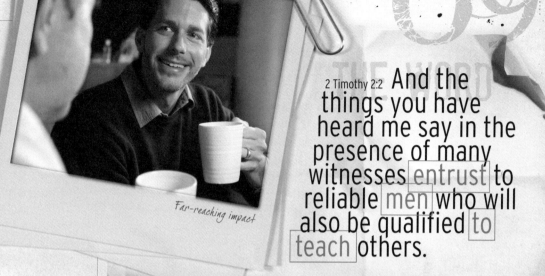

Far-reaching impact

2 Timothy 2:2 And the things you have heard me say in the presence of many witnesses entrust to reliable men who will also be qualified to teach others.

think it over...

1 What opportunities do you have in your current post to support students or younger doctors?

2 Could you consider working with CMF now or in the future?

3 How can you plan now to make it happen?

TAKE HOME MESSAGE: CMF needs you!

> *Let my heart be broken with the things that break God's heart*
> *Bob Pierce*

Volunteer your time

You hurt me so much. The final result of our relationship was the conscious choice to take the life of our baby. And this left me heartbroken.' Painful words from a post-abortion client, but she is not alone. Our city-based crisis pregnancy centre has been providing post-abortion counselling to a steady stream of deeply distressed women. Some come to us just days post-abortion, but others talk about terminations they had 10 or 20 years ago! We offer a ten step support programme that facilitates grieving, accepting responsibility and invites them to consider forgiveness as a way forward. Sometimes, not always, they will ask God's forgiveness and put their hearts right with their maker. But every one of them experiences Christ's grace and love through their Christian counsellor. They learn that 'mercy triumphs over judgment'.

The Christian crisis pregnancy movement has grown exponentially since the first centres were opened in the late 1980s. There are now 140 centres across the UK, a national helpline and a website with an online advisor facility for anonymous counselling. Supported and resourced by CareConfidential, a national umbrella organisation, this movement is a spontaneous, compassionate, grass roots response by Christian people to the challenge of abortion.

Not surprisingly, some centres struggle to gain acceptance with secular health professionals and statutory bodies, many of whom are suspicious that Christian counsellors will coerce or manipulate women into not choosing abortion. It is somewhat ironic, therefore, that secular pro-choice counsellors are assumed to be entirely objective!

Christian judgment

Infinitely more puzzling and painful is the negative response sometimes encountered from fellow Christians. Some believe that our centres offer abortion as an equal value option alongside parenting or adoption, and see such counselling as devoid of moral boundaries and indistinguishable from the secular, pro-choice counselling available at BPAS and Marie Stopes.

Their strategy would be to avoid non-judgmentalism and openly tell women that choosing abortion is wrong. But, as Joanna Thompson, CareConfidential's former director, said ,'...just telling women they must keep their babies often causes them to protect themselves by hardening their hearts and justifying further their right to abort'. In our experience, most women choose abortion out of a mixture of fear and misinformation. Therefore, we aim to empathise with the woman's very real and painful dilemma by demonstrating compassion and respect. We offer practical support to help her conquer her fears and hopefully choose the life affirming options of parenting or adoption.

Using our post-abortion counselling experience, we can provide accurate but painful information about the possible risks of abortion. We help with the mechanics of decision making and ensure it is a properly informed one. But that decision remains hers. Like God, we respect her moral decision; our hearts are pained if she makes the wrong choice, but we are there should the consequences of her choice prove overwhelming.

Truth and love

No Christian crisis pregnancy counsellor would ever recommend a woman to have an abortion; it is never a counsellor's role to tell someone what to do. And yet, in most societies, abortion is a live, legal option for women facing a problem pregnancy. It has to be discussed. As Christians we wish, like Jesus, to be 'full of grace and truth'; at our centres we aim to speak that truth with love.

Roslyn Holzman wrote as a crisis pregnancy counsellor and **Sara Kundu** wrote as a child psychiatrist

LINKS

Triple Helix, 2007. www.cmf.org.uk/literature/content.asp?context=article&id=1992

Ephesians 4:15 ...speaking the truth in love, we will in all things grow up into him who is the Head, that is, Christ.

Serve your community

VIEW TWO

Parents who form secure attachments with their infants will have children who are more socially competent, self-confident, popular, resilient and mature. Sadly the reverse is true of insecurely attached mother-infant pairs. When parenting goes wrong, children suffer. Their development goes astray, resulting in emotional and behavioural difficulties. Families characterised by conflict, aggression and cold relationships have children vulnerable to psychosocial problems, substance abuse and problems with biological stress-response regulatory systems.

We have seen remarkable changes in the lives of many families

Church parenting

At the Good Shepherd Mission, a church in the London Borough of Tower Hamlets, we started running parenting courses using Family Caring Trust materials alongside our parent and toddler group in 1999.

Our aim was to improve the mental health of both children and parents, reduce risks of abuse and later antisocial behaviour, and promote happier, better functioning family lives.

We also adapted Family Caring Trust's optional session on children's spiritual development to suit our own approach and found it an excellent opportunity to engage in respectful discussion about spiritual matters with parents who were interested.

We now receive referrals from local GPs and health visitors and have developed a working relationship with the local Sure Start Centre. We now also use the Incredible Years programme for families with more severe needs. We have seen remarkable changes in the lives of many families: parent-child relationships have blossomed, children's behaviour has improved and parents have said how much less stressed they feel. In some, we have also seen spiritual change and growth. For us, these are very good recommendations for any church or other organisation wishing to serve its local community.

think it over...

1 How would you counter the argument that non-directive counselling by a Christian simply condones abortion?

2 How might you sensitively be able to bring subjects like forgiveness into a discussion about abortion?

3 Almost every specialty deals with children or parents. What can a doctor do to help parents?

TAKE HOME MESSAGE: Practical action often shows God's mercy more clearly than words

121

work

Reflecting Christ in the workplace

I believe one of the next great moves of God is going to be through the believers in the workplace.
— *Billy Graham*

've just about had enough. I'm getting out!' How many times have we heard this? How often have we thought it? In Britain, we so often hear of stress, burnout and post-traumatic stress disorder. Healthcare professionals are not the only ones to witness one tragedy too many or simply to suffer from being overstretched. In his incarnation Jesus too suffered fatigue. At times, he felt quite overwhelmed by the horror that lay ahead of him, but received grace and strength to go through with it. He knew the fullest force of temptation because he never yielded, and now knows exactly how we feel when we are tempted to give in, give up or get out.

When Paul was persuaded to leave Ephesus, he knew arrest and possible death lay ahead but still longed to complete his appointed task. Much in his letter to the young Ephesian church is still relevant and encouraging to those working under pressure today. He reminds us of our calling, our competencies and the character God has in mind for us.

Our calling – Ephesians 1:3-14

Even though writing from prison, Paul quickly turns to praise. He lists the many blessings given to those who, through Jesus Christ, have been adopted into his family, chosen by God with the thrice-mentioned intention they should live to his praise and glory. This repetition should make us ask how we come across – not only when wearing shining going-to-church faces, but also in the workplace. The church is the body of Christ, not just a building. So, whether we are in our consulting rooms, operating suites or committee meetings, there is the church. God is bringing all things under the headship of Christ so this must include everything that happens at work.

Therefore, our ultimate authority is not our own

Janet Goodall wrote as an emeritus consultant paediatrician

autonomy, primary care trust, health authority, or even the Minister of Health, but Christ himself. Assurance that all new edicts, difficult patients and ethical dilemmas are to be dealt with 'to the praise of his glory' should help us to look trustfully to God for the wisdom and understanding 'lavished' on us for times like these, rather than letting ourselves get anxious, frustrated and exhausted.

Our competencies – Ephesians 4:7-13

We are reminded we have been called by God, so are not just doing a job but fulfilling our vocation. We are all told to be humble, gentle, patient and loving; but we also need to find our particular God-given competence and use it in the workplace. Yet since the Fall, 'subduing the earth' has been hard and burdensome. Many around us still complain bitterly that, rather than subduing their workload, it is subduing them! It is in Christ that we can receive God's redemption and abundant supply of grace, raising us up to enjoy his gifts. Christians should not join the chorus of moaners but instead act as encouragers and burden-sharers.

Just as God elected in the early church apostles, prophets, evangelists, pastors and teachers, so we should find distinctive, perhaps parallel, gifts in each other for use in our professional callings. Paul claimed those who had believed through his ministry as the seal of his apostleship. Many Christian doctors experience this same seal, even when not widely known as wonder-workers. Some of our patients have been prompted to put their faith in Christ simply because we have, even unconsciously, acted as channels of his love to them.

By applying biblical principles and being open to the Holy Spirit, some are enabled to 'prophesy' the results of a particular course of action, both in consultations and on committees. Through a divine nudge,

Triple Helix, Summer 2006. www.cmf.org.uk/literature/content.asp?context=article&id=1840

It could be that our God-given gifts are primarily intended for use in the mission field of our daily workplace

A vocation: not just a job

Ephesians 5:1-2 Be imitators of God, therefore, as dearly loved children and live a life of love, just as Christ loved us and gave himself up for us as a fragrant offering and sacrifice to God.

an unconscious foretelling, our words might be used to avert an approaching disaster, perhaps within someone's relationship. It can be easier for practitioners of front line (rather than back room) medicine to see themselves as pastors, whereas others know that their special competence is in administration or simply the ability to help others.

Our character – Ephesians 5:1-21

'Be imitators of God.' What an ambition! This only becomes a possibility as we allow God's Spirit to fill our lives, especially producing his first fruit of love. As the Spirit of Jesus gradually works the necessary transformation, the intended image of God emerges. The alternative is to be moulded by the image of the world about us, whose ugly manifestations stem from something else having taken God's place.

Since Paul forewarns us about this in detail, we should take careful note. We must be on our guard against unsavoury gossip, coarse jokes, foolish – and possibly complaining – talk, as well as sexual immorality. Temptations attack when punishing rotas keep us away from Christian friends or family, but being unemployed can leave us equally vulnerable. We are instead to 'find out what pleases the Lord', namely goodness, righteousness and truth, and to let Christ's light shine on any shady areas.

The passage ends by going back to 'everything' – the 'all things' that we have often found hard to cope with, or even considered walking away from. We have been reminded of our calling along with unique competencies for use in his service. His goal is to develop our characters to become like his. No wonder we are challenged to a new attitude in the workplace. Still thinking of getting out? First make sure that you have invited him in.

*This article is based on a talk by **Canon Mark Brown** at a CMF day conference*

think it over...

1 If asked, would your consultant know you were a Christian? Would your junior colleagues know?

2 What might be your spiritual gifts? Discuss them with another believer. How might they be used in a medical (rather than church) context?

3 Are there any particular temptations at work which you need to avoid?

TAKE HOME MESSAGE: We must take Jesus to work with us... he isn't just for Sundays

No person shall be under any duty ... to participate in any treatment authorised by this Act to which he has a conscientious objection.
Abortion Act 1967

abortion requests

The theory of abortion ethics is discussed elsewhere (Think 5 and 7). But what should we do as an F2 or registrar in general practice, when a patient is sitting in front of us, asking to be referred for abortion? Four Christian GPs explain how they handle it.

Jim Newmark – 'I have been a Christian doctor for very nearly a third of a century. You would have thought I would have this issue just about sorted, but I do not. I remain confused. My take is from the perspective of a jobbing frontline Christian GP who personally has never (yet) signed a blue form, but does not object to making a written referral to hospital.'

He goes on to say that those who refuse to make a written referral ignore 'the inevitable consequences to other doctors, whether they are Christian or not, who are now consequently, and inevitably, caught up in the issue. Like the unborn child, they are ignored, a by-product of events out of their control... I think what has happened in Christian circles is that people have paid too much attention to the theoretical objections as a proxy for their "personal integrity", and have lost sight of the magnitude of the consequences... in the real world to others. And I have a sneaking suspicion that there is at least some element of one-upmanship in the sense that "by invoking my right of conscientious objection I am a better Christian than you".'

He summed up '...a doctor cannot un-know what he/she knows. In virtually all these situations in real, as opposed to theoretical, general practice, the doctor is a participant, albeit unwilling – end of story. I think that, too often, Christians use the conscientious objection clause without really thinking about what it means either for themselves or for others.'

Andrew Fergusson wrote as CMF Head of Communications

Mark Houghton – 'I offer patients four things:

■ **Respect** – for the mother, baby, father and family
■ **Review** of knowledge to fill in the gaps about the fetus, social services, and so on
■ **Regard** for the law which does not permit abortion on demand
■ **Referral** as a last resort

The woman may arrive scared, angry, hurt and confused. I explore opportunities to find joy, because she is carrying a new person. A colleague of mine said to a woman: "You might be carrying the next Beethoven". Years afterwards she would bring the boy in, smiling, "Here is Beethoven"!

We can choose non-cooperation and non-referral to stress a corrupt system into change – or we can combine to invoke the law. The UK Abortion Act is weak but exists to protect the woman and baby. As a last resort the law offers hope for my little patient. And it may save her mother from death because abortion is more dangerous than a delivery. If she is determined on abortion I write a detailed, referenced letter concluding "I find no grounds in law for this termination request. If it happens I would consider it illegal. The peer-reviewed evidence is below."'

Rhona Knight – 'I do what I aim to do in all consultations. I take a history, clarifying the presenting problem and identifying the patient's ideas, concerns, thoughts, fears, and expectations and why they have them. I explore external pressures compromising free choice. Having reached a shared understanding, I then hope to negotiate a management plan, in which evidence-based medicine and values-based medicine both play an intrinsic part.

The negotiated way forward, like each consultation, is unique. It may include time for reflection, or accessing other pregnancy support

LINKS *Triple Helix, 2010. www.cmf.org.uk/publications/content.asp?context=article&id=25516*

Christian doctors will not all be identical in practice, but mercy and compassion must underlie the choices we make

What shall we do??

organisations, or bringing the patient back to see a colleague who would refer for abortion if this is what the patient chooses. In this overall approach, I hope I am making the care of the patients my first concern, demonstrating love for neighbour, born and unborn, while also working as part of a wider team who may have differing ethical beliefs.'

Greg Gardner – 'It is extremely rare for a woman to be refused an abortion by an abortion provider. Referral for a "second opinion" is nothing of the sort. It is referral into a system which fast tracks pregnant women to one outcome only. Failure to screen women adequately for risk factors prior to abortion is negligent and failure to tell a woman if she does have risk factors for post-abortion injury is also negligent. Women need access to evidence and information – and time to think.

There is no legal right to abortion. The Abortion Act merely decriminalises abortion if certain criteria are satisfied. Among these are that the risk to the mother's physical or mental health would be greater if she continued with the pregnancy than if she had an abortion. Although a risk assessment has to be made in each case, there is enough evidence already of hidden and delayed maternal morbidity and mortality and this undermines the legal basis of virtually every abortion done in the UK.

How ethical is it for GPs to refer women into the abortion pathway? It depends on what your view is of complicity. At the very least it could be construed as endangering someone's life since this referral route almost always results in the death of the unborn child. It is entirely reasonable to decline a woman's request for referral to an abortion provider.

ed's thoughts...

Though most Christian doctors would be against most (if not all) abortions in principle, the opinions here show that there is not agreement on how this works out in practice. There is lots to consider – our own personal conscience, the wishes of the mother, the unborn baby, current abortion law, and the views of a society that largely supports abortion. We should always remember that patient as we think about our response, and remember that the way in which we deal with them as a person will make as much (if not more) impression on them as our carefully worked out ethical response.

think it over...

1. What are the medical things you would need to get right in an 'abortion request' consultation?

2. How can you prevent a similar situation occurring in future?

3. What is the patient likely to be worried about? How can you address her concerns?

4. Christian doctors don't all agree! What are your feelings about each suggestion above?

Every week a boy with black curly hair and a red and black striped jumper would bully a boy waering glasses. This was classed as popular entertainment.

03

Bullying

Wouldn't you think that, being such a grubby and cowardly business, bullying would be quite ashamed to show its face? Yet it is alive and well, an integral part of NHS culture. It thrives on silence and secrecy but, brought out into the open, it looks altogether less frightening. Yet many people don't believe that reporting a bully would change anything except their own position for the worse.

Bullying is the abuse of another person by virtue of some sort of power over them. Bullying is not the ordinary rough-and-tumble of two sinners trying to relate to each other. You know the difference: the colleague who makes you feel cold just by being there; that loathsome, manipulative patient; your managers trying to horse-trade another encroachment on your peace of mind; the consultant who can't lead without humiliating others.

Humanists say that bullying is unacceptable because no one has a right to a lifestyle that degrades other people. Christians go further: when you degrade another person, you insult their Maker.

Firm supervision or bullying? – Supervision and mentoring are meant to be formative, but should never be destructive: reducing self-esteem and ability have no place in a supervisory relationship. Most NHS trusts have formal anti-bullying policies, but these frequently go the way of all other well-meaning policy statements when push comes to shove. In one study of junior doctors, 37% said they had been bullied in the last year, and 84% in their professional lives.

Mark Cheesman wrote as a consultant geriatrician

What can you do if bullied?

Write – Strip the incident of emotion and record the bald facts. Write it down and then read it. Is it reasonable to be upset by this? If so, take it to someone you trust and ask for their judgment. Write, time and date all such incidents: this will be invaluable if you decide to pursue things.

Think – Try to separate the just from the unjust. We do need to learn from our mistakes even when the rebuke was unreasonable. If harsh words were justified, accept them.

Before undertaking a difficult conversation remember that the other person is precious to God

Decide – If it's not a big deal, go and talk to them. Choose your time well: say what you think they did wrong without emotion and offer your hand. If they have any integrity, you'll go up in their estimation.

If it is a big deal – repeated, malicious or sexual bullying – don't do anything on your own. Sift through your thoughts with a trusted third party – a chaplain, colleague or BMA representative. Together, explain to the bully why their behaviour is unacceptable and how you will respond if it's repeated. Briefly record the proceedings afterwards.

In either situation, a variety of reactions is possible. The bully may be astonished and apologetic. You might encounter cold resistance. Remember, it is not your job to produce repentance – you want the behaviour to cease.

Going nuclear! – Like resigning, you can do this only once. Your 'superior' colleague has far more to fear from it than you do. A serious, evidence-based accusation of bullying is a devastating thing to face. It also effectively ends the relationship. Sometimes it might have to be done: for the sake of others, justice and the honour of your Lord. It involves putting in a formal complaint,

LINKS *Triple Helix*, 2004. www.cmf.org.uk/literature/content.asp?context=article&id=1194

testimony

A **former GP registrar says...** My problems started when I moved to a new training practice for my GP registrar year. On the surface, my trainer seemed friendly but had an unpleasant habit of twisting everything I said, making a mental note of it, and then later using it against me.

Amid false accusations, my paperwork would go 'missing'. It was impossible to find the culprit as the staff would back each other up. It would have been easier if they had been verbally abusive to me - rather than this psychological undertow.

It came to a head when I made a serious mistake which was in every way my own fault. I was visibly upset at work one morning and my trainer started to goad me, saying that this affront was the latest in a long line of misdemeanours that he wasn't prepared to discuss with me. I then blamed my behaviour on a non-existent family 'crisis' hoping that he would leave it at that. He subsequently discovered that my family were fine.

I was publicly humiliated and after a short period of unemployment was moved to another practice for a further six months. Things were instantly easier and I have since thrived.

Beware of defining as intelligent only those who share your opinions. – Arthur Block

backed by records and advice. It's unpleasant, destructive and causes significant collateral damage. The bully knows this too and will be just as anxious as you to avoid it. Threaten only once and then do it.

Pray – Prayer is a wonderful transformer – of us, promoting God's will on earth, not ours in heaven. We can bring any trouble and ache to our Heavenly Father. Sitting in silence with God is transforming. Slowly, we gain heaven's perspective on the situation: then it's relatively easy to pray for the most disagreeable person. Jesus' name can bring down extraordinary barriers.

The power of 'No' – Most of us worry too much about refusing to be abused. As I have progressed as a consultant, I have been struck by how few adverse events there are when you say 'No'. After all, the only person we have no right to say this to is God. Now, your manager is not God.

Proverbs 17:5 **He who mocks the poor shows contempt for their Maker; whoever gloats over disaster will not go unpunished.**

think it over...

1 Can you think of incidents where you or others around you have been bullied?

2 As you get more senior, how will you avoid the temptation to bully junior staff?

3 Think of someone you struggle with at work, and remember that they too are made in God's image. How will this change the way you relate to them?

TAKE HOME MESSAGE: **Act carefully, dispassionately, and early**

conflicts

Claire chose her first job because she really clicked with the Christian consultant. Unfortunately, things have changed recently. The consultant has become part-time, now only covering outpatients; Claire no longer has regular contact with him. The new locum ward consultant is unapproachable and impossible to please. Even worse, Claire's immediate senior sits in the mess 'supervising' Claire doing all the work: she issues orders rather than requests and never says please or thank you. Whenever Claire makes a mistake, her senior has a good laugh about it with everyone else in the mess. Claire bursts into tears during FY1 teaching, blurting out that her senior is horrible to her. Rumours start. The senior accuses her of bitching and then tells their Christian consultant that Claire is incompetent and difficult to work with! Claire has now lost all her self-confidence and feels inadequate as a doctor. She also feels a bad witness: she should be turning the other cheek, not grumbling. What should she do?

This scenario contains familiar elements that we've all faced. Claire is disappointed: two difficult bullies have replaced her idealised Christian consultant. Malicious gossip thrives in NHS culture and takes innocent victims. Work-related stress is an issue: events have snowballed, resulting in Claire's tearful breakdown. Tiredness and fragmented Christian connections make us forget that we are 'works in progress'. We often beat ourselves up regarding our own failings.

Liz Croton wrote as a senior house officer

Disappointing fellowship

Regular fellowship with other Christians, particularly senior colleagues, can be immensely comforting. Sadly, this is not usually the case and we can really feel for Claire, being landed with these two difficult individuals instead. Although often surrounded by his disciples, Jesus did spend time in solitary communion with his Father. Although Christians are sometimes without fellowship, we are never alone.

Gossip – Is such fun! Christian or not, we all love a good nugget of another's misfortune. Still, it's not godly behaviour. Proverbs 11:13 hits the nail on the head: 'A gossip betrays a confidence'.

Stress – Claire's breakdown illustrates the 'put your head down and get on with it' NHS mentality. Nipping problems with difficult colleagues in the bud is hard. Constant activity and ongoing stress can lead to outbursts.

A bad witness – We have clichéd ideas of the perfect Christian: a witnessing expert who faces injustices and trials with a cheesy smile! We can all sympathise with Claire's guilty feelings, which reflect her humanness and weakness. Yet she is allowing the Devil to gain a foothold.

What now?

Claire needs sound godly advice on managing this situation in a Christlike manner. She should approach her educational supervisor for help.

It would be wise to talk to her Christian consultant as he is senior, knows Claire well and is already involved. Could he act as a godly arbiter while they air their grievances and find a solution? Some new FY2s or ST trainees find having their own juniors very difficult. Claire's senior may not even know that her behaviour is unacceptable! Also, it is important for Claire to examine herself as well. It is easy to blame her senior, but there may be aspects of Claire's personality and habits that are irritating, leaving her partly at fault.

LINKS Triple Helix, 2004. www.cmf.org.uk/publications/content.asp?context=article&id=1261

Verona writes... I once worked in a challenging department. Even the most straightforward issues were blown out of all proportion. I'd been in difficult situations before but never had I seen such a general environment of confusion, manipulation and sometimes downright ridiculous behaviour patterns.

There were many aspects of it that weren't healthy. As I reflect, I know that it taught me so much. The first thing I had to do was to acknowledge who God is, and then repent of my part in the antagonism, gossip and bad behaviour. I had to address that first. I had to search out and celebrate the things that were lovely, true and noble in the situation − for example my growing friendship with the nurses − and praise God for them and how they were sustaining me.

I had to understand that the forces at work were of the spiritual realm and that I needed the full armour of God to stand and not crack up! I used the word of God as the sword of the Spirit to know what was true and what wasn't. I looked at Jonah − I, too, may have been a reluctant prophet, but God had anointed me to bring his light into the darkness in that place.

Practically, I galvanised others to pray for me. I did much more listening and praying than speaking. I also found ways that were more appropriate to express myself, particularly when battles were raging all around.

Dominic writes... Generally I try to avoid conflict. 'If it is possible, as far as it depends on you, live at peace with everyone' (Romans 12:18) would be my maxim at work. I also try to be helpful where possible. This sometimes involves chatting to people, even when perhaps I could be using the time to do something more overtly worthwhile, for instance to write a report on a patient. When conflict arises it is always best to know what position the other person is coming from. I try then to build bridges using common ground where possible. If conflict is inevitable over an important matter of principle then I marshal my forces, for instance consulting others and planning carefully. Once when I couldn't resolve the conflict even after two or three years of trying, I was about to leave the post. A combination of prayer and talking to a senior manager, led to the person I was in conflict with actually leaving, instead of me.

Malicious gossip thrives in NHS culture

Proverbs 26:20 **Without wood a fire goes out; without gossip a quarrel dies down.**

think it over...

1 What can you do day-to-day to reduce stress in your workplace?

2 How might you deal with someone who is a source of stress?

3 What action might you take to ensure you can talk to Christian colleagues?

TAKE HOME MESSAGE: **Conflict is to be expected, but help should be sought early if it becomes a source of stress**

WORK 05

Contraceptive requests 05

A **16 year old girl comes to see you wanting to start on the oral contraceptive pill.** What advice can you give her about the available options? What might you as a Christian be able to bring into this consultation that most GPs wouldn't bother with?

Initially you need to take a good history that includes gynaecological basics such as details of her menstrual cycle. You also need to consider the reasons behind her request. Before launching into a lecture about contraception, make sure you have elicited all her ideas, concerns and expectations.

Comprehensive history

Is she in a sexual relationship? If so what method of contraception, if any, is she using? Has she had any casual sexual relationships? Is she being put under unwelcome pressure to sleep with her boyfriend? After that you are in a strong position to move on to counselling her about her various options.

In medicine today there is a strong culture of ensuring that patients are fully informed about their decisions.

Fully informed consent

Unfortunately in the areas of abortion and contraception this is generally not the case. Side effects of abortions, especially psychological, are glossed over, and there are many women who have no idea how their contraception works. It is our responsibility as Christian doctors to ensure that our patients can make fully informed choices about any medication they take or procedure they undergo. We should not use tactics of scaremongering, but we should speak the truth in love so that they

John Wenham
wrote as a GP

understand the consequences of their chosen course of action.

Once you have explained the options clearly you may want to offer your patient the chance to ask questions or to go away and consider her options. If she chooses a method that largely relies on preventing implantation, what will you do? Will you prescribe it?

> It is our responsibility as Christian doctors to ensure that our patients can make fully informed choices about any medication they take or procedure they undergo.

Sharing God's wisdom

Finally, at some point you should look for the opportunity to share some of God's wisdom with your patient: 'Why not wait until you are sure that the person you are going to have sex with is committed to you long term?' Genesis 2:24 is God's plan for us and we would do well to remind others of it. The teenage pregnancy rate in the UK remains the highest in Europe. In the USA some schoolchildren are taught to wait until they are ready – it's cool to be a virgin. Challenge the status quo and prick some consciences on the way. In some cases it will open doors for further discussion about your faith.

Nucleus, Spring 2003. www.cmf.org.uk/publications/content.asp?context=article&id=344

testimony

Helen says... As a junior doctor, working for a short time in general practice, I didn't have the chance to build up a group of regular patients. Consequently, young patients often chose to come and see me as I had free appointment slots. Many of these were young women either wanting repeat contraceptive prescriptions, or exploring starting on the pill.

I was careful not to prescribe the morning after pill, or repeat requests for the progesterone only pill, but with hindsight I wonder if I should have used these opportunities to engage the patients in conversation, particularly the teenagers. At no point did I attempt to convey a biblical perspective on God's intentions for sex and family. Instead it was all too easy to ask all the routine questions, type out the repeat prescription, usher the patient out, and feel a sense of satisfaction that my appointments were all running to time.

John says... Deciding which contraceptive to recommend is never easy. I'm convinced that life begins at conception, and is worthy of protection from then. However, many patients don't share this view, or (more often) have never thought about these things. As a GP registrar, I spent a lot of time reading about the mechanism of action of progesterone-based contraceptives, and IUCDs. The only answer was that we don't know the answer! The literature surprisingly pointed towards a pre-conception action for the morning-after pill for example, but with little certainty – which didn't help much!

It was clear that we don't entirely know how all contraceptives work; the evidence is constantly changing. I became wary of taking a dogmatic position, and even more careful to make sure patients were fully informed about how their drugs worked. It is easy to be so black and white in our position as to be inconsistent – for example not prescribing the morning after pill because we think it acts after conception, but forgetting that the combined pill may also occasionally act in this way. Whatever we choose ultimately to do, it is important to keep up to date, and explain the truth as far as we know it to our patients.

Explain the truth as far as we know it

ed's thoughts...

Though unwelcome, underage sex is a fact of life in our society. We may want to reverse this trend, but need to ask ourselves where the best place is to do this. There may be much we can do in the consulting room in the conversations we have; others may prefer to take part in sex education teaching in local schools, or promote public health campaigns aiming to delay first intercourse. Outright refusal to provide contraception is sometimes suggested as an option, but is practically very difficult, and risks ending any further dialogue with the patient.

think it over...

1 How does the above scenario change if the person asking for contraception is aged 15? Or 13?

2 How much is it your place to give advice regarding delaying intercourse?

3 Christians do not always agree about which forms of contraception are acceptable and which are not. Can you defend your own views?

4 What method would you personally use if and when married?

5 How do you reconcile the patient's autonomy to choose the contraceptive they want with your autonomy to prescribe in line with your conscience?

> When you face a crisis, you know who your true friends are.
> *Magic Johnson*

Crisis Management

Alex's night is not going well. Whilst clerking down in A&E, a ward he's only just left calls him, wanting an opioid prescription. He runs back up. Bleep: the lab have thrown away a sample he spent an hour extracting from a violent, demented lady, all because he misspelt her name! Bleep, bleep: someone else wants to self-discharge! Bleep, bleep, bleep: when will he be returning to A&E?! Tired, stressed and hungry, he loses his temper and snaps down the phone at the A&E nurse. He shouldn't be behaving like this but...

Pit stop!

We both remember nights like this all too well! Alex is over-worked and under-rested but his bleep is firing on all cylinders! In the race that is a medical on call, a brief time-out can improve a doctor's performance, so benefiting everyone. Even the Great Healer took his team away to eat and rest when things got too hectic. So, Alex could lock himself in the toilet for five minutes! NHS loos are well-recognised safety valves.

Resuscitation

Even the prophet Elijah snapped! Tired, stressed and hungry, he wanted to die. God provided food, time out and rest... before sending him on to his next assignment. Once Alex has regained emotional control, he should attend to his physical and spiritual survival. What about shooting arrow prayers: 'Lord God help me!'? A quick wash and drink are excellent pick-me-ups. Alex's next destination should probably be the nearest vending machine... Munching on a Mars Bar (if there's nothing healthier on offer), Alex could make a cunning plan:

Damage limitation – No-one likes being snapped at but most nurses are amazingly forgiving. A&E nurses are particularly flexible and helpful. A sincere telephoned apology could do wonders for the rest of Alex's night in A&E! He could even ask her to apologise on his behalf to his waiting patient.

Prioritisation – try listing bleeped requests as 'urgent', 'this shift' or 'next shift'. Let people know where they stand, for example: 'Thanks for letting me know about this. I'll get onto it by the end of the shift'. There is nothing non-Christian about reminding others that you only have one pair of hands and legs! If people argue with your prioritising, turn to...

Negotiation – Alex could have given that ward nurse three options: accept a non-opioid verbal, do nothing until he could leave his higher-priority patient, or send an HCA down with the drug chart. This last option would have satisfied him, the nurse and the patient!

Delegation – Alex's team should be brought in to help, and jobs reallocated where possible. Be clear about which team member you're asking to do what and that (s)he is proficient in the necessary skills.

'But I'm a Christian...'

Irritable sleep-deprived Christian medics often feel guilty. Yet our bodies are not meant to function without sleep or nourishment. An irritable remark certainly isn't a positive witness, but a sincere apology from a tired medic is a rare thing and people do sit up and notice. If you're usually irritable when sleep-deprived, it may be worth apologising in advance.

Sleep, sensible meals and time with God are absolute musts. A plethora of Christian meetings (however worthy) is unlikely to refresh, but a relationship with God should take priority. This does not necessarily mean a regular quiet time or weekly church attendance. Regular chats with a 'soul friend' may be better than dozing through Bible study groups!

Rachael Pickering and **Helen Johnson** wrote as GPs

LINKS *Triple Helix*, Autumn 2004. www.cmf.org.uk/literature/content.asp?context=article&id=1243

Beena says... Looking back on my first few months as a house officer, I realise now just how needlessly frazzled I was. Yes, the job was busy, but I made it much more frantic by not being as organised as I now have learned to be. Thankfully, during my second house job, my registrar diagnosed the cause of my perpetual franticness and gave me a crash course in the art of prioritisation. It worked wonders for my stress levels and really improved my on-call relationships with nurses and patients alike. Now that I'm a reg myself, I make sure that all my FY1s know a bit more than I did at their stage about coping with relentless workloads.

Over-worked and under-rested?

Mark 6:31 **...they did not even have a chance to eat, [Jesus] said to them, 'Come with me...to a quiet place and get some rest.'**

John says... Covering the wards was much easier once I started to note down not only the task needed after a bleep, but also it's priority. Sometimes a bit more information is needed to do this - for example if three patients on three different wards are short of breath, knowing the oxygen saturation, respiratory rate and admitting diagnosis for each of them makes it much easier to choose who to see first. Nurses occasionally need prompting for this information, but most are helpful - seeing, I think, that I was taking the call seriously by trying to find out more.

Looking to the future

Alex may find such awful nights becoming rarer as he gains experience, but even seasoned juniors have the occasional nightmare shift. If his problems continue, Alex should confide in his tutor. He could also contact the Doctors' Support Network, and see his GP; he may be at risk of burnout and depression.

TAKE HOME MESSAGE: **Prioritise, negotiate, delegate**

think it over...

1 For fy1s and fys2
How do I deal with bleeped requests at the moment?
Am I naturally an organised person?
Could adopting the prioritise, negotiate, delegate approach make a real difference to my stress levels at work?

2 For more seasoned juniors
Do I check that my fy1s aren't drowning in a sea of non-urgent jobs?
Is the prioritise, negotiate, delegate approach something I could teach new doctors?
What other approaches to crisis management have I learned?

Discussing death

On the world nothing can be said to be certain except death and taxes.
Benjamin Franklin

'**That injection killed him!' 'He was the kindest man who ever lived' 'The hospital never told me he was going to die!' 'We did everything together...' These are just some of the things that have been said to me as a GP after a patient's death.**

Comfort and compassion

At a deathbed we are confronted with our own mortality and our dependence on God; we doctors are more likely to help our patients and their relatives if our whole lives and the way we practise medicine reflect this dependence. We are not in control, but 'we can comfort those in trouble with the comfort we have received from God' (2 Corinthians 1:4) when our behaviour (including the way we may touch someone or allow them to cry) demonstrates compassion. We need to listen carefully, speak the truth and, as the Spirit gives opportunity, offer words of hope.

To comfort someone is to give them strength to face their situation as it is; so we need to give relatives unrushed time, acknowledge that our patient has died, and express our sympathy. They may have questions or comments and our first duty is to listen. Asking questions – what actually happened or how the rest of the family are – may help someone to get talking.

Life after death

After expressing sympathy, clarifying the facts and listening to relatives, there may be opportunity for us to give a word of hope or simply to start talking about the next chapter in their lives. It is not our sole responsibility to help relatives in bereavement, a process that takes time. Our role is to make ourselves available and let them choose how much they want to

Kevin Vaughan wrote as CMF Head of Graduate Ministries

see us. Raising a personal faith flag like 'I do believe there is hope after death' may be appropriate and I have found that relatives may welcome an offer to pray with them. Yet we must act with 'gentleness and respect'. If relatives show signs of not wanting to talk yet, we should withdraw, leaving a clear signal that we are available if required.

To comfort someone is to give them strength to face their situation as it is

We do not want to be a Job's comforter of whom he said, 'miserable comforters are you all! Will your longwinded speeches never end?' The Old Testament tells that, when Jacob heard of Joseph's presumed death at Dothan, 'All his sons and daughters came to comfort him, but he refused to be comforted'. May God help us to know when to keep silent.

I have known relatives come to faith in Christ after the death of some of my patients. I'm sure that, if we are prayerfully sensitive to the Spirit's leading, God will give us opportunities to speak of him in a way that will help some relatives move closer to a relationship with him. In my experience though, others will often be involved in this process: even by simply encouraging relatives to get in touch with a church or another Christian, a doctor may be doing something that makes a difference for eternity.

Triple Helix 2007. www.cmf.org.uk/literature/content.asp?context=article&id=1905

testimony

Howard says... I picked up the consent form and made my way towards the patient's bed but was intercepted by her daughter. 'You're not going to tell her what she's got, are you? She wouldn't want to know, she couldn't cope.' Mrs A was an alert lady in her seventies suffering from ocular malignant melanoma and I was preparing her for eye surgery the following day. She seemed to be keen to know her diagnosis and as it was her eye that was going to be removed, I explained to her daughter the need for informed consent. 'No, please do not tell her – it will worry her' she replied.

As a Christian I felt very uncomfortable withholding such information, so I asked my consultant to obtain consent for the operation. Colluding with relatives may seem kind, but patients who want to know deserve the truth, and the opportunity to prepare emotionally and spiritually for whatever the future may hold.

Compassion needed

2 Corinthians 1:3-4 **Praise be to the God... of all comfort, who comforts us in all our troubles, so that we can comfort those in any trouble with the comfort we ourselves have received from God.**

Linda, a hospice counsellor answers some questions... **Does your faith affect your work?** Immensely – although by no means everyone working here is Christian, having a belief in life after death really helps in hospice work. It helps me be sensitive to people's spiritual needs. We work closely with our chaplains, one of whom is also the hospice's chief executive! Occasionally, people prefer to talk solely to the chaplains, thinking that the word 'counsellor' has psychiatric connotations!

What communication tips could you give?

Make time. Book them a double GP appointment. See them at the end of your list. Go back to them at the end of the ward round. Rapport is everything; don't talk down to patients, sit at their level.

Don't assume. Check out what is written in clinic letters or notes about a patient's understanding of their illness.

Slowly slowly. Practise asking open-ended questions about how much they know. Take it step by step. Respect a patient's decision not to know.

Watch an expert. Most hospice doctors and oncologists are experts in the art of gently breaking bad news.

think it over...

1 Have any deaths of patients particularly affected you?

2 What could have been done better when these patients died? What was done well?

3 Some would say we are taking advantage if we talk about Jesus with a dying patient or their family. How would you respond to this?

TAKE HOME MESSAGE: **Discussing death needs time... along with gentleness and respect**

Always be prepared to give an answer to everyone who asks you to give the reason for the hope that you have. But do this with gentleness and respect
1 Peter 3:15

Sharing Christ with Colleagues

Picture the situation: you're a hardworking, frequently stressed junior doctor in a busy hospital. The firm is close-knit, supportive and your colleagues are all good mates.

Five o'clock comes, you jet off home swapping your stethoscope for a Bible. Home group is your next stop. You're actually a committed Christian doctor but nobody at work knows. You see you'd rather they didn't find out what extracurricular activities you get up to. Sharing the most important part of your life with colleagues can be indescribably difficult at times.

Do we dare to be different or do we resign ourselves to being 'private-life' Christians? What would Jesus have us do? Jesus' earthly ministry was scandalous in the frequency with which it broke social norms and conventions. Similarly he commands us to do the same. We do not belong to the world – we have been called from it. Jesus has explicitly commissioned us to make disciples for him from all nations. We should not delay.

If we examine closely what we are being commanded to do, it all seems like a pretty tall order. We are after all friable human beings. Thankfully we have been blessed with the gift of the Holy Spirit, which does a very good job of helping us in our weaknesses and our efforts at evangelism.

Do not be ashamed to testify

We have the Spirit on board, so what comes next? 'Faith comes from hearing the message', states Paul in his letter to the Romans. While we busy ourselves living out good lives among the pagans, there may well ultimately come a time when we are called to give account for our faith and present a Gospel outline to our colleagues.

Liz Croton
wrote as a surgical SHO

So, you're going to share the Gospel with a colleague. The pair of you are having lunch together but the opportunity never arises. Disheartened you head to the mess where about 20 of your peers are watching MTV. One guy asks why you weren't at the drug dinner last night? 'Oh I was at church,' you reply. Silence falls while several pairs of eyes swivel in your direction waiting for you to explain yourself. Now, in which situation would you rather talk about Jesus? The young apostle Timothy was command by Paul to 'preach the Word in season and out of season'.

A stubborn refusal to disrespect our seniors whatever their actions is a powerful witness to the grace of God

Over to you

So the proof of the pudding is that we can share Christ with our colleagues and impact their lives. We have to be receptive to God's call, immerse ourselves in his Word and dare to be different! There are so many people who have never heard the Gospel or alternatively think they know what it's all about and have dismissed it as irrelevant. We will rub shoulders with many people like this in our walk through medicine. Let us not be frightened to use these opportunities to make our Lord known.

LINKS   *Nucleus 2001. www.cmf.org.uk/literature/content.asp?context=article&id=374*

testimony

Andrew says... I have found that my faith as a Christian can be a bit of an enigma for my hospital colleagues; there doesn't seem to be a box to fit me into. I have conservative moral views, like the Muslims, but unlike the Muslims I will join in the hospital socials and have fun. I will drink but not get drunk and arrange my annual leave around church events, but won't seem to make a big deal of Christian holidays. I am 'religious' but seem very different to the typical hospital chaplain.

This creates a great opportunity for conversation and I have found work colleagues to be some of the most open people I have come across. Hospitals are very pluralistic; with Sikhs, Hindus, Muslims and atheists all working alongside each other. When I have taken genuine efforts to understand their worldview, asking lots of questions, people have been extremely open towards the gospel. My greatest joy came when my nominal Hindu friend from medical school became a Christian at my church last year. It had been nine years of friendship, with lots of socials and holidays together, that culminated in him saying that he knew Christianity was genuine because he saw it lived in people's lives.

Roger says... When the opportunity comes (as it surely will if you pray), will you know what to say? I arrived at university struggling even to articulate the gospel clearly in my own mind - let alone to anyone else. Although my personal understanding improved quickly, it was not until a CMF *Confident Christianity* course when intercalating that I felt able to articulate the gospel clearly to student colleagues.

The course helped me not only to present the gospel, but to feel prepared for the inevitable questions. I remember one conversation at a BMA conference where it seemed as if the colleague I was talking with must have overheard one of the courses, simply because he asked all the questions I'd learnt how to answer!

Although conversations about the gospel don't always come that naturally to me, it is a lot easier now that I can be confident I know what to say – and it does get better with practice and prayer!

Many of the best conversations come with a cup of coffee

Romans 10:17 **Faith comes from hearing the message, and the message is heard through the word of Christ.**

think it over...

1 What can you do to ensure your colleagues know you are a believer, (other than preaching at them)?

2 What situations at work might provide opportunities to speak about the gospel?

3 Have you considered how you might answer questions that medics commonly bring up (suffering, creation / evolution, sexuality)?

TAKE HOME MESSAGE: **Our work is a great opportunity to make Jesus known**

Surviving FY1

> Let us not give up meeting together, as some are in the habit of doing, but let us encourage one another
> Hebrews 10:25

Almost everyone survives medically during FY1 jobs, but many suffer spiritually. We must aim to thrive as believers, not simply survive. Here are some thoughts and ideas to enable you to thrive:

Maintain your devotional life. The author of Psalm 1 seeks his delight in God's law, rather than the counsel of those around him. Find time for some formal Bible study and reading of Christian books. Even when busy, there are spare moments of time to be with the Lord, but patterns may have to change from those of student life.

Maintain Christian fellowship. The writer of Hebrews exhorts readers to continue to meet together to encourage one another. Many of us will have been richly blessed with Christian fellowship as students, much of which may suddenly disappear when starting work (especially if moving to a new area). It is important to seek out believers quickly. Finding a church is important.

CMF can also help! There is a pastoral care scheme that links junior doctors to a local CMF member who can provide fellowship, friendship and maybe recommend a church. A junior doctors' conference is run each autumn, and there are junior doctors' 'open house' groups operating in an increasing number of cities. If there isn't one near you, why not start one?

Keep in touch with some non-medical Christian friends as well – I was greatly supported by believers who knew me well but had nothing to do with medicine and could give a wider perspective.

Take evangelistic opportunities. The great commission still applies as an FY1! Be known as a believer from day one, perhaps by talking about church activities if asked how you spent last weekend. This means that a godly life will be associated with Christianity, rather than you just 'being a good person'.

Watch your lifestyle. The Ephesians were reminded to be 'imitators of God', and to live a life of love. Those around us rarely share our values, and we may think that we can get away with things, especially if there are no other believers around. Gossip, alcohol and sex are constant issues. If lonely you may be more susceptible to sexual temptation than you have been as a student.

It is imperative that we do our job to the best of our ability. Not only will our Christian witness be blunted if we are perceived as bad doctors, but there will be fewer obstacles to our walk with God if we work efficiently and quickly – for example, it will be easier then to leave on time to get to house group.

Keep in touch with some non-medical Christian friends as well

Maintaining integrity is vital. It is so easy to exaggerate the severity of a patient's condition to get a scan done faster, or to say that you have done something when you have not. Know where your competency ends, and call for help if that point is reached. Record that you sought advice, and what action you took as a result.

Build relationships. Most will be short-term – although they may be intense at the time. Try to learn the names of non-medical staff on your ward. With a few patients, you can go beyond simple physical medicine. This is not only part of good medical care, but may lead to opportunities to share your faith as well.

Manage time well. Jesus had more demands on his time than he could immediately meet. He managed this by setting his own priorities.

In the work environment, the key is to prioritise. Is it important for you to do? If so, do it now if it is urgent, schedule it if it is not. If it is not

Laurence Crutchlow wrote a few months after completing his house (now FY1) jobs in London

Nucleus, 2004. www.cmf.org.uk/literature/content.asp?context=article&id=724

testimony

Robert says... There can be some fun as an FY1 as well as work. On a cold, January on-call night, I was bleeped to see a patient who was complaining of being too cold. I arrived at his side room to find that following recent building work, there was a gap of about two inches between the window frame and the wall! My treatment for this was to get up on a chair and place masking tape over the hole to insulate the room. Although I hadn't been taught this at medical school, the patient seemed especially pleased with my management plan – and I had great fun writing the ensuing incident form!

Kerry says... FY1 is not all doom and gloom. There will be times when you get to pause in that busy day at work and smile, as you realise a precious moment has just passed. I worked on a relatively busy cardiology firm for four months as an FY1, and I will never forget the day when one of our consultants asked us, in a pause on our morning round, for some feedback on how we felt the job was going. As we made the tea, a couple of us muttered the usual: It's good, I'm learning a lot and I'm enjoying it phrases until one of us, a fellow FY1, piped up and said 'There should be more chocolate'. Realising that she had said this out loud, her face dropped into a mortified expression. We all burst out laughing, consultant included, and continued with our ward round. Ever since that day, there was always plenty of chocolate to go round the team on consultant ward round days. :)

important for you to do, try to delegate it if it is urgent. If it is neither important nor urgent, question whether anyone needs to do it at all!

Get adequate rest. Jesus rested and prayed. There are very few situations that will be made worse by a 20 minute delay for you to eat lunch. Try to take advantage of natural breaks in the day. Your performance suffers when you are tired, affecting patient care.

Know your ethics. You may be surprised that this has been left until last! Although important, neglect of devotional life, lifestyle and witness at work are more common causes of Christian FY1s struggling with their faith.

Build relationships

Luke 5:16 **But Jesus often withdrew to lonely places and prayed.**

think it over...

1 What times of your working day might allow quick, one-off prayers?

2 How can you maintain Christian fellowship in your current job?

3 What do you do to make sure you get enough rest?

TAKE HOME MESSAGE: **Maintain your spiritual life, and other things will naturally follow**

09

141

Heartsink patients

I find being a GP quite draining at times and it can be difficult to motivate myself especially when faced with a long list of patients with varying problems.
A GP in North London

Midway through afternoon surgery as a GP trainee, you notice a cancelled appointment, and start thinking of the coffee you will now have time to drink! The next patient is a teenager who you give a little extra time, and you finish seeing her with five minutes of the spare appointment left. You mark her has having left on your appointment screen, and notice that the cancelled appointment has been filled by a 65 year old man who is well known to you, and you abandon all hope of coffee, or of leaving on time.

What is it about this patient that causes your heart to sink? Most patients booked at the last minute have very simple problems. A few can be seriously ill, but for most GPs appropriately treating and referring these patients is satisfying, even if it causes surgery to run late.

But there is a small cohort of patients who fill most doctors with dread. Perhaps surprisingly for those who haven't worked in general practice, these are not the very sick or aggressive patients. The typical 'heartsink' usually has a multitude of symptoms, but few (if any) verifiable diagnoses. Usually attending frequently, they are often keen to see the same GP each time – often for reasons that are not immediately apparent.

Patients of this nature are not confined to general practice. Many A&E departments have a number of 'regulars' who attend frequently with unexplained symptoms. Pain clinics often see people with symptoms that are difficult to explain, and even surgeons and gynaecologists often have patients who repeatedly appear in clinic with vague symptoms, despite normal investigations.

Laurence Crutchlow
wrote as a GP

What is the problem here? Sometimes the difficulty is the doctor, or the medical profession more widely. It is understandable that patients become frustrated when there is no medical explanation for their symptoms. Problems may be psychological in nature, but patients often feel 'fobbed off' if such an explanation is offered – particularly if it is done in a way that implies their symptoms to be false. Over-investigating usually doesn't help, and sometimes doctors fail to diagnose underlying anxiety or depression in these patients.

The typical 'heartsink' usually has a multitude of symptoms, but few (if any) verifiable diagnoses

Occasionally the problem lies directly with the patient - but actually very few people deliberately set out to irritate or exhaust their doctor, even if it doesn't always feel like that in a busy surgery!

I've come to realise that more often the problem is loneliness, and lack of community. Nearly all the patients like this that I've seen have been isolated – either living alone, or unable to talk to their families or friends about problems. Regular attendees at A&E often feel they've nowhere else to turn – even if their problem is obviously (even to them) neither an accident nor an emergency.

Gradual breakdown of communities increases the number of people who feel isolated. Here the church has a role to play. Where can people who are lonely turn? Where will someone find an unconditional welcome in their community? Often it is to the door of the GP that the lonely turn, knowing that it will be a place where they are listened to, and not judged. How would our communities (and surgery lists) look if the church were the first place people turned?

A problem shared

A physician is not angry at the intemperance of a mad patient, nor does he take it ill to be railed at by a man in fever. Just so should a wise man treat all mankind, as a physician does his patient, and look upon them only as sick and extravagant
Lucius Annaeus Seneca

testimony

Marvin says... Even a few weeks as a GP registrar or FY2 will often give rise to a few 'heartsinks' – patients who conjure up dread whenever their name appears on the appointment screen. There may be legitimate reason for this feeling – the patient may be rude or abusive, or perhaps has genuinely complex problems. Some will be drug or alcohol dependent. More often 'heartsink' patients are those with numerous symptoms, but few (if any) verifiable diagnoses.

In common with most GPs, I don't find them easy to deal with. It's essential early on in treating them to get a good handle on what has and hasn't been done medically for them. Constant repetition of tests will probably make things worse – but take care before assuming 'it's all in the mind'! It is easy to miss something in a patient like this, as their diverse presenting symptoms occasionally mask a serious underlying pathology.

I've found it helpful to (gently) tackle the reason for their repeated attendances once I've got to know them a little. Sometimes a myth needs to be dispelled – for example 'my incapacity benefit level will go up if it's on my records that I see the GP a lot'. At other times patients simply haven't understood what they've been told – and a simple explanation can often help. A persistent worry about an already excluded condition may indicate underlying anxiety or depression.

Beyond all the medical techniques (which are things any GP, not just a Christian, might use), I constantly need reminding that difficult patients are still patients needing care, as well as God's creations. They need to be treated respectfully – in the context of trying to manage their consumption of scarce resources.

1 John 4:11 Dear friends, since God so loved us, we also ought to love one another.

think it over...

1 Can you think of any 'heartsink' patients? What is it about them that makes you feel that way?

2 What steps can you take to tackle someone who repeatedly consults in general practice, or is seen thrice weekly in A&E?

3 Try thinking of a difficult patient as a creation of God, loved by him. How might this lead you to treat them differently?

TAKE HOME MESSAGE: **All patients were created and are loved by God**

Surviving night shifts

The current world record for the longest period without sleep is 11 days, set by Randy Gardner in 1965
BBC science

The 91-hour week that can be clocked up when doing seven consecutive nights has been suggested to be dangerous for both patients and doctors. Evidence from the USA suggests that serious medical errors increase by one third when doctors' hours lengthen from 65 to over 80 in a week. The risk of being involved in a road accident while commuting was shown to rise by 16% for those working these longer hours.

Ensure you are not overtired before your nights start. Don't start the week with no petrol in the car and no food in the house. Accept that you will do little else between shifts than travel, eat and sleep. It may be best to go to bed at midday and get up at 7.30pm, much as if day and night were reversed, but this can be difficult if it is too light or noisy at home.

Make sure you don't dehydrate. Many try to survive nights with urine outputs that would have nurses calling for a doctor urgently! I find sleeping in quiet patches helpful, but not everyone agrees. There is some evidence that short naps do help: a NASA field study amongst pilots suggested that a 40 minute nap produced a 34% increase in performance and a 54% increase in psychological alertness when compared with no nap.

Working efficiently is vital. Take a handover, familiarising yourself with the sickest patients. Get routine jobs sorted out first, so that only emergencies need concern you in the early hours of the morning. Set a plan for any difficult patients at the beginning of the shift. Treat ward emergencies definitely when you see them – there is not usually time to 'wait and see'. But remember that much can (and often should) wait until morning.

You cannot hope to be refreshed the next evening if you do not leave on time. In a shift system, it is inevitable that work will be passed on. Don't feel guilty about this, but also expect to take on handed-over work at the start of a shift. Some post-take rounds run well into the day, and you will need to ask to leave on time. You are not going to learn anything from the round if you can't stay awake. I found most consultants to be sensible about this - in fact quite a few would send me home themselves – but you may have to take up any problems with those responsible for monitoring your hours.

How can your relationship with God fit into such busy weeks? Church and house group meetings are hard to attend. Formal quiet times may be difficult. Yet our relationship with God is not just a function of scheduled activity. We are commanded to pray constantly. Gaps during work allow prayer, and these may be more frequent at night. In addition, it is possible to pray while working, perhaps when waiting for a bleep to be answered or for the blood gas machine to process your ABG. There is often time to read a pocket Bible or quickly log onto *Doctor's Life Support* on the CMF website. I found increased opportunities for meaningful conversations at night, particularly with colleagues.

Night shifts are an exercise in practising the presence of God, learning to depend more on his personal relationship with us than on formal structure. God's promises are enduring, and he won't withdraw from us simply because we are tired or can't be at church.

Frequent blocks of nights may have an impact on our relationship with God and our fellowship with other believers. If we are called to career choices that involve many years of night shift work, we must evolve coping strategies and trust God to help us. If repeated nights are still a stumbling block after a while, we should consider whether God really wants us in such an acute field.

Laurence Crutchlow wrote as a GPVTS SHO

LINKS   Triple Helix, 2006. www.cmf.org.uk/literature/content.asp?context=article&id=1842

Judgement is often worse during night-shifts – particularly between 3am and 7am – double-check your work to be safe

Night shifts: practise the presence of God

1 Thessalonians 5:17-18 **Pray continually; give thanks in all circumstances, for this is God's will for you in Christ Jesus.**

testimony

Kim says... When I am on nights – it's lonely, I get tired and snappy and I feel I am less forgiving. The frustration can sometimes be heard in my voice on the phone, and it's hard to stay cheerful when you are under pressure to get so many tasks done. Then I meet some fantastic nurses during the night, who manage to stay cheerful and even help me out by re-writing drug charts for me to sign and I feel slightly embarrassed, because they are also under pressure. There are moments during the night when things seem to be getting too much, and that's the point when I should take a moment to say a prayer and ask God to help me be patient with others, but I don't always do that. It is our actions and our attitudes which others will notice and Philippians 2: 14-15 is worth keeping in mind – 'Do everything without grumbling or arguing, so that you may become blameless and pure, children of God without fault in a warped and crooked generation'.

TAKE HOME MESSAGE: **God is still present on a night shift – even if you don't feel like he is**

think it over...

1 How much work do you do during an average night that could have been done in the day?

2 What can you do in your daytime work to reduce the load of the doctor on nights?

3 Do you always get away at the end of a night on time? Can you change this?

4 Could you get involved with rota design and try to avoid long blocks of nights?

The Lord has anointed me to preach good news to the poor.
Isaiah 61:1

Sharing faith with patients

I n the gospels Jesus asks questions wherever he goes and we would do well to follow his example. It is now well recognised that holistic care is part of the service that all doctors should offer and the Royal College of General Practitioners' curriculum requires 'the development of a frame of reference to understand and deal with the family, community, social and cultural dimensions in a person's attitudes, values and beliefs'. By asking questions, we will not be expressing our own personal beliefs, but rather exploring those of the patient. This is part of good clinical care and may on occasion also open up further conversation, when the doctor is free to share something in response to the patient's comments or questions.

Spiritual history enquiry essentially involves three areas:

Belief
- 'Do you have a faith that helps you (in a time like this)?'
- 'Do you have a personal faith?'
- 'What is important to you?'
- 'Do you believe in God?'

Religious practice
- 'How does it affect your life?'
- 'Have you ever prayed about your situation?'
- 'What principles do you live by?'

Faith community
- 'Who gives you support?'
- 'Do you belong to a church/faith community?'

One doctor attended a *Saline Solution* conference organised by CMF and heard of these questions for the first time. She was keen to try them in the surgery the following week, and when she was reviewing a patient whom she had been seeing for two years, she simply slipped in the question 'Do you have a faith that helps you?' This took the patient by surprise and she initially gave a hesitant reply. The doctor wisely let the matter rest there for that day, but on subsequent visits the patient opened up greatly, there was opportunity to pray together and, encouraged gently by the doctor, she started attending a local church. What double joy! Joy for the doctor, as she discovered that God may open a door when we ask a simple question; joy for the patient, as she was able to discover Christ following a conversation with her doctor.

As Christian doctors we will not want to force our views on anyone

Faith flags

When exploring the spiritual needs of people dying of lung cancer or heart failure, Murray *et al* found that, sadly, many patients expect that doctors will not be interested in spiritual issues, even though they themselves would like to talk about them.

In order to identify ourselves as people who care about spiritual matters, it can be helpful to raise a brief faith flag in conversation. This should be unforced and appropriate to the moment. A simple comment like 'Some of my patients say prayer helps' or 'It makes a big difference to me to know that there's someone up there looking out for me' puts no pressure on patients or relatives, but gives them permission to raise spiritual concerns if they so wish.

Just before an Easter Bank Holiday I recall asking a patient what she would be doing over the weekend. She described how she would be caring for her sister who was dying of breast cancer. She then asked me what

Kevin Vaughan
wrote as CMF Head of
Graduate Ministries

LINKS *Triple Helix*, 2008. www.cmf.org.uk/publications/content.asp?context=article&id=2112

testimony

Gareth says... I don't share Christ with everyone I meet and sometimes I can go months without telling anyone about him at all. I have found three tactics useful. First, I wear a cross or fish. This can encourage believers, so that they often ask you to pray with them, and perhaps they will pray for you, and also to act as a possible conversation starter. Second, I try to keep an eye on the locker of each of my patients. If the Gideon Bible has moved, I ask them about it and what did they read? Often this will start a conversation. Third, I try to ask if they have any religious beliefs when I take a social history. I used to cringe when I started doing this but people can happily answer 'C of E' or 'None' without embarrassment, while a Jehovah's Witness might be glad you asked. The next part is answering their questions and I would recommend a *Confident Christianity* or *Saline Solution* course for anyone who feels they need practice or more confidence.

Sometimes the only certain thing we can give is Jesus

1 Peter 3:15 Always be prepared to give an answer to everyone who asks you to give the reason for the hope that you have. But do this with gentleness and respect.

I myself would be doing, and when I mentioned that Easter was a special time for me and my family as we would be remembering how Jesus died and rose again for us, she immediately burst out 'Oh! I wish I could have a faith like that!' This opened the door for further conversation.

If our relationship with patients is built on the foundations of clinical competence, trust and good communication, the atmosphere of mutual respect will usually help the doctor to know how and when to speak sensitively and appropriately about spiritual matters. However, we will need courage and compassion for our patients, and we will need to be praying for the Holy Spirit's guidance and wisdom every day.

We will also need to be prepared to justify our actions if we face criticism from patients, relatives, colleagues, or even the GMC for what we say. May God give us all the grace and wisdom we need to be appropriate witnesses for him in our everyday life.

think it over...

1 Can you include a spiritual history when seeing a patient? Can you teach students to do the same?

2 What 'faith flags' can you think of in addition to the ones suggested here?

3 Could you pray at the beginning of each day 'Lord, show me one person to pause with today'?

4 Could you answer the common questions that might arise from the gospel message?

Truth and integrity

Have the courage to say no. Have the courage to face the truth.
Do the right thing because it is right
W Clement Stone

VIEW ONE

The scenario... at times, life as a hospital junior can feel like a never ending game of piggy in the middle. It's no picnic when you're squashed – like the meat in a sandwich – between two large personalities with opposing priorities and opinions. You know what we're talking about... The consultant who wants a CT scan versus the radiologist who insists it's not indicated... The reg who wants a D-dimer at 3 am versus that technician who won't get out of bed to do it... the scenarios are endless.

Dr Diplomat

Along with my MBChB, I often think that having a degree in diplomacy would often come in really useful! After all, juniors often have to act as go-betweens for senior staff and other departments.

Top tip!

To avoid problems arising from unnecessary or inappropriate requests, why not ring up beforehand to make sure that the test you have in mind will actually yield the information required? Get yourself ready first with the patient's details and a concise history. Take previous films down to the radiology department if there isn't an electronic system. Write requests legibly and don't miss out relevant details such as your bleep number.

Nothing but the truth?

As a Christian I try to be truthful at all times, but it is tempting to bend this rule when caught between a rock (your rather fierce registrar) and a hard place (the radiology department). Routine tests are the hardest to justify: how many normal chest X-rays have I seen on post-take ward rounds?! At times I've not been sure why my patients required particular tests, making it difficult to give relevant details on the forms and giving rise to several sticky situations. I found discussing tests with my seniors a useful learning tool: their differential diagnoses were often different to mine. Are we trying to differentiate between diagnoses, confirm a suspected diagnosis or rule another differential out?

On the defensive

The rise and rise of defensive medicine is a related issue. Requesting tests in order to rule out diagnoses is becoming more and more common. There is no easy solution to this. Increasingly, both radiology departments and labs are swamped with requests. We do have a responsibility to use tests wisely, consider costs and think about risk versus benefit for each patient. On the other hand, I have found myself considering the potential costs – financial and emotional – of complaints for missed diagnoses. If I miss a diagnosis through neglecting to request a relevant test, it won't be the radiology consultant having to explain himself!

At the end of the day, as long as the test I've requested is relevant and has potential benefit to my patient, I am happy to ask people to accommodate extra patients or even get the radiology registrar out of bed. Caring for your patient can mean standing your ground and asking your seniors to back you up.

Emma Hayward wrote as a Paediatric SHO on a VTS rotation and **Richard Mainwaring-Burton** wrote as a Consultant Biochemist

LINKS

Triple Helix, 2005. www.cmf.org.uk/literature/content.asp?context=article&id=1644

THE
Leviticus 19:11 **Do not** steal. Do not lie. Do not deceive one another

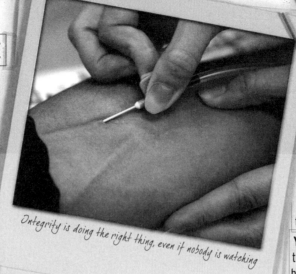

Integrity is doing the right thing, even if nobody is watching

Petty bureaucracy? A phone call during one of my weekend consultant biochemist on-calls: **'I'm having some trouble with one of your technicians – she won't let me come down to the lab and label a blood sample!'** I hadn't been anticipating trouble as the biomedical scientist working this shift was one of our best team members. 'That is according to our protocols', I replied. 'How can you be sure it's your patient's blood?' 'It's the only one I've taken so it must be...' 'How many other samples do you think our lab's received today?' The discussion continued. The SHO admitted that he'd left the unlabelled bottles with a nurse, expecting that she'd label them before sending them up the chute. Clearly there'd been a misunderstanding between doctor and nurse!

Our practice must be safe at all times. Analysing a blood sample of unproven identity is not only dangerous but adds considerable doubt to the relevance of the results. Hence our apparently draconian policy: it's there to protect the laboratory, the clinician and above all the patient.

Scapegoats
Cynicism born of years of disappointment makes me suspicious that what happened next was, 'Sorry – there's been a laboratory error. We're going to have to take more blood.' It does happen. As a patient myself, I have heard reference to laboratory error. And why not? Possibly the relationship between patient and doctor is more important than my technician's integrity. Indeed, I almost regard this role as one of the responsibilities of the unseen services.

Resources
Analysing unlabelled samples can be seen as uneconomic, as the results may well be ignored or repeated. Unnecessary investigations are wasteful and strain service departments' budgets. They could also be regarded as assaults upon patients! We all have a responsibility regarding proper use of the materials at our disposal and clinicians working at the coal face are not exempt from this.

A matter of protocol
Departments develop protocols, usually in agreement with clinical colleagues, to control inappropriate use of tests. Although these protocols should be respected, deviation from them should be flexible and negotiable, but only through proper channels. I personally regard a request for any investigation as a referral to another clinical discipline, so it would be good to have confidence in the information provided. Doctors providing misinformation on GP or interdepartmental referrals are not long in developing unfavourable reputations!

think it over...

What are the implications of telling the truth for you and the patient in each scenario?

You are a GP FY2. A patient missed a court appearance four days ago and now wants you to provide a sick note for that day, stating he was vomiting. He hadn't seen you (or anyone else in the surgery) on the day in question.

You see a patient in gastro clinic. He is very clear that he doesn't want you to write down in his notes how much he is drinking.

Your registrar arrives at work smelling of alcohol. He realises you've noticed, and he doesn't want anyone else to know. Later, your consultant asks whether your registrar is alright, he's noticed he looked unwell. What do you say?

resources

cmf books

Many of the pieces on this book are edited versions of longer, fully referenced articles, available on the CMF website. Please see the links on individual pages to find these.

A number of other CMF publications provide useful more detailed information about the topics covered here.

CMF Files
More than 40 of these have been produced, covering topics such as 'Health Benefits of Christian Faith', 'Organ donation', and 'Resource Allocation'. About 3,000 words in length, they are written at a simple level, and can easily be given to a non-medical friend.

The CMF Blog
Gives up to date information from CMF on current issues.
cmfblog.org.uk

Helpful recent CMF books on ethics include:

At A Given Moment
Graham McAll
Discusses sharing faith with patients

Matters of Life and Death
John Wyatt
Background and more detailed information on ethics, focussing mainly on beginning and end of life

Hard Questions about Health and Healing
Andrew Fergusson

Mad, Bad or Sad
M Dominic Beer and Nigel D Pocock
Exploring a Christian response to mental illness

Complementary and Alternative Medicine
Robina Coker

All these and many more are available to order online at *www.cmf.org.uk/bookstore*

websites

One is always wary of including websites in a printed publication, as many good sites go offline, or change their stance. The following few may be helpful, along with those referenced in original articles from the book.

- **Cambridge Papers**
  Produced by the Jubilee Centre, these quarterly papers examine a current question from a Christian perspective. Those on money and wealth are particularly helpful.
  www.jubilee-centre.org/cambridge_papers

- **Christian Institute**
  Their website hosts for free a number of their publications of interest to Christian doctors. *www.christian.org.uk/resources/publications*

- **Care Not Killing**
  This alliance of which CMF is a part campaigns on end of life issues.
  www.carenotkilling.org.uk

- **Christian Medical Comment**
  The personal blog of Dr Peter Saunders, CMF Chief Executive; mainly on medical issues (with the occasional diversion into New Zealand and rugby!)
  www.pjsaunders.blogspot.com

- **British Medical Association**
  The website tells you how to get involved, as well as hosting a lot of employment and pay related information. Some of it is members-only access.
  www.bma.org.uk

CMF
Christian Medical Fellowship

The Christian Medical Fellowship

was founded in 1949 and has over 4,000 doctors and 1,000 medical students in the UK and Ireland as members. We are linked with around 70 similar bodies worldwide through the International Christian Medical and Dental Association (ICMDA).

Members come from all Christian denominations and are united by their faith in Jesus Christ, their belief in the Bible as God's word, and their calling as doctors, medical students, and other professionals working in healthcare.

The CMF logo

The 'triple helix' represents the three persons of the Trinity – Father, Son and Holy Spirit – as well as the tripartite nature of humanity – body, mind and spirit. The cross is at the centre because we believe it is Jesus Christ's death and resurrection that make our relationship with God possible, and Christ's example of service in carrying the cross that inspires us in our own service in medicine.

Our aims

- **Discipleship** – to unite Christian doctors and medical students in Christ, and to encourage them to deepen their faith, live like Christ, and serve him obediently, particularly through acting competently and with compassion in their medical practice.

- **Evangelism** – to encourage Christian doctors and medical students to be witnesses for Christ among all those they meet.

- **Mission** – to mobilise and support all Christian doctors, medical students and other healthcare professionals, especially members, in serving Christ throughout the world.

- **Values** – to promote Christian values, especially in bioethics and healthcare, among doctors and medical students, in the church and in society.

Our activities

About 25 staff based in our London office or around the country help members keep in touch, co-ordinate our busy conference and publishing programme, and provide support and advice.

Much of the Fellowship's work depends on the commitment and involvement of grassroots members who serve on committees, organise events, pray, give, write, speak, support each other and take new projects forward. There is plenty of scope to get involved in specific areas of CMF's ministry that God lays on your heart.

Uniting Christian doctors

In almost every medical school and in most UK regions local groups of doctors and students meet regularly for teaching, encouragement, fellowship and support. National and regional weekend and day conferences run throughout the year and we encourage CMF 'communities' that enable members to cultivate special interests with like-minded colleagues.

Increasing Christian faith

We provide training to help doctors, students and other healthcare professionals to practise medicine that meets the needs of the whole person, and to help them share their faith in general conversation 'with gentleness and respect'. We organise breakfasts, evening meals and dialogue events where colleagues and others have the opportunity to hear the gospel and a Christian viewpoint so they can raise objections, engage in discussion and have their questions answered.

Promoting Christian values

We play a strategic role by providing thoughtful and clearly written resources for students and doctors, and by making authoritative submissions to government and other official bodies. We also equip Christian doctors and students to speak out personally: in the NHS, the BMA and Royal Colleges; through government; and nationally and internationally in Christian, secular and medical media.

153

Advancing Christian mission

We help support over 200 members working abroad full time, with a variety of mission and secular agencies in 45 different countries. Another 200, based in the UK, make regular short-term visits to support teaching and training. We run workshops throughout the year and a two week course in the summer to equip people for work in the developing world.

Publishing Christian literature

Our regular publications *Triple Helix* (for graduates), *Nucleus* (for students), *CMF News*, and *CMF Files*, together with a number of different websites and a host of books, CDs and other resources keep members informed and up to date on all things Christian and medical. *www.cmf.org.uk* is always a good place to start.

Supporting Christian students

CMF has a vibrant student ministry with around 1,000 medical student members. Students benefit from conferences, literature, local support and international links.

Why join CMF?

There are personal benefits for members through receiving literature and resources, and through getting involved in our conferences, events, local groups and training. But mostly membership is an opportunity to share in our work - building Christ's Kingdom in and through Christ-centred healthcare.

Where does CMF's support come from?

It comes almost entirely from our members. CMF is a registered charity and annual income and expenditure significantly exceed £1,000,000. Of this about a third comes from members' subscriptions, and most of the rest from members' donations and Gift Aid. Detailed accounts are available on request.

Who can join?

Everyone in sympathy with the aims of CMF, who can also sign the membership declaration, is welcome to join. If you are not a doctor or medical student, you are welcome to join as an associate member.

What is the membership declaration?

'I am in sympathy with the Aims of the Christian Medical Fellowship. I declare my faith in God the Father and in God the Son, the Lord Jesus Christ, who is my Saviour, and in God the Holy Spirit. I accept the Bible as the supreme authority in matters of faith and conduct.'

Which membership is for me?

- **Doctors** - those in full-time practice
- **Medical Student** - for medical students
- **Associate** - for anyone else

Concessions are available for doctors who are part-time, retired, married or working in developing countries.

How do I join?

Join on line at *www.cmf.org.uk*. Alternatively, you can also contact CMF by phone: 020 7234 9660, or by post: Christian Medical Fellowship, 6 Marshalsea Road, London. UK, SE1 1HL

How do I find out more?

Please feel free to telephone, email, or visit *www.cmf.org.uk*

now you can become a...
friend of CMF

Looking for guidance from a biblical perspective on end-of-life care, abortion, infertility, contraception and a range of other healthcare issues? The **Christian Medical Fellowship** wants to help you to address the growing number of issues at the interface of Christianity and medicine.

Regular e-mail updates will equip you to:

- **make informed decisions** about healthcare
- **support Christian doctors and other healthcare professionals**
- **engage in the national debate** on healthcare issues
- **respond with Christ's compassion** to the healthcare needs of the poor

It's free to become a Friend of CMF - sign up at www.cmf.org.uk/friends